Pottery Science

CERAMIC SKILLBOOKS

Series Editor:
Murray Fieldhouse

Pottery Science

The Chemistry of Clay and Glazes Made Easy

Martin Wickham

PITMAN/WATSON-GUPTILL

PITMAN PUBLISHING LIMITED
39 Parker Street, London WC2B 5PB

Associated Companies
Copp Clark Limited, Toronto
Pitman Publishing New Zealand Ltd, Wellington
Pitman Publishing Pty Ltd, Melbourne

First published in Great Britain by Pitman Publishing Ltd 1978
Published in the USA by Watson—Guptill Publications 1978

© Pitman Publishing 1978

WATSON—GUPTILL PUBLICATIONS
a division of Billboard Publications Inc.,
1515 Broadway, New York, NY 10036

UK ISBN 0 273 01189 8 (cased edition)
UK ISBN 0 273 01193 6 (paperback edition)
US ISBN 0-8230-4223-5

Text set in 10/12 pt IBM Century, printed by photolithography,
and bound in Great Britain at The Pitman Press, Bath

Contents

Acknowledgements

My thanks must go in the first instance to my wife, Jenny, for holding things together while I sat and mused. Also to my typist, Wendy Smith, for all her conscientious work, and to the Thursday Group for asking the right questions. I should also like to thank the following for lending their work to be photographed: Jeanette Arkinstall, Joyce Hendrie, Kathy Shadwell, Pam Williams.

Particular thanks are due to David Phillips for encouraging me to put pen to paper, and to David Lewis and Cathy Gosling in the preparation and editing of the book.

Introduction

Anyone with the slightest pretentions to being a scientist should stop reading now. A scientist will be annoyed at the use of non-scientific language, confused by the reverse order in the presentation of scientific data and impatient with the number of words it takes to put over so slight a scientific truth.

This book assumes that the reader has no aptitude and little interest in the disciplines and scope of the sciences. It assumes that he or she is predominantly interested in the tactile and visual possibilities of clay and it accepts that many will approach the book half believing that their time would be better spent making pots. For these reasons I have deviated considerably from the standard approach of most text books. If you like, this little volume may be considered as a primer to more formal works and may succeed in bridging the gap between the artist and science. I hope, however, that there is enough substance in it to allow the least scientific potter scope for considerable experiment.

The primary question I have asked myself throughout is whether this book will make the reader a better potter? I have concentrated on that information which will increase the visual possibilities open to the potter and which will help overcome simple problems. It is necessary to introduce 'pure' science occasionally to provide a basic coherence, but I have tried to keep it no more than one step away from practical ceramics.

1 Glazes Without Chemistry

Before we look at the chemistry of glazes let us consider how an experienced studio potter might go about evolving a new glaze, and in so doing show how little chemistry is used. Potters haven't the time to turn their workshop into a laboratory — they want quick and, above all, successful results. Businesses do not survive on exciting failures.

First, the potter does not start from nothing; nor does he start from higher chemistry. He starts from tradition. Pottery is all about tradition. All studio pottery techniques have a long history, so have the different firing temperatures and kilns used. In the same way, good glazes have honourable ancestries. A glaze which has been used successfully by generations of potters and in a variety of conditions is precisely the sort of glaze the potter wants. When a potter looks around for a new glaze, he starts from something tried and tested. This is not so narrow and academic as it may seem, for the more fundamentally stable a glaze, the more the potter can experiment with it and still expect good results.

Where does the potter find recipes for such glazes? He may ask amongst his colleagues and try glazes from manufacturers, or, more experimentally, refer to books. Professional potters rarely get more experimental than this for it is not necessary. Potters have not usually got the time to try to create a new basic glaze from random material. They may experiment to some extent with wood ash, feldspars and clays which are satisfyingly basic but which in fact have been very well tried in the past and various broad proportions worked out. However, these very crude glazes, while often giving interesting results, are usually too unpredictable to use in the studio. At this point the reader may be wondering why he or she should bother with chemistry and experiment if everything is so formalized. But people do not stop painting in oils because they no longer have to grind their own colours. They accept from the manufacturers a concoction with a label such as Vermilion and then see what they can do with it. Potters go one step back and do effectively grind their own colours as often as not, but the recipe they initially work to is an established one.

How should you, the beginner, start to build up a catalogue of glazes? Well, how have you learnt about coiling? From a book? Then look in books for glaze recipes. Do you attend classes? Then find out what glazes are used. Whatever point of contact you have with established potters, use their experience by starting from their glazes. If the potters themselves are cagey about parting with recipes, write to art colleges, or buy glazes direct from pottery suppliers. In this way you will get sound glazes which can be experimented on.

The most important thing to do is to get some good recipes together. Why bother further then? The point is that obtaining a good basic glaze is the starting point, not the end point, of a potter's experiments. The rest of this book is intended to help you make informed guesses as to what to add to a given glaze.

Let us suppose that a potter has tried a batch of half a dozen different glazes from books, all professing to give exciting results. For a variety of reasons many recipes will not have worked. For example, a book originating in a foreign country may give good glaze results using ingredients from that country, and on that country's particular clays, but may give awful results in the

Test tiles made from small slabs (1 x 1½ inches). One basic glaze with different quantities of colouring oxide.

changed situation. It is possible that one will have worked very well. This usually means quite simply that this glaze fitted the potter's clay. It neither ran nor crawled, blistered nor crazed, nor produced any detrimental side effects. It would also have given a finish that looked promising. The colour or opacity may have been wrong, or in some other way it may not have been suitable for the ware he was making, but the portents would be good. It is part of the experience of a potter to recognize possible successes from failures and to know how to rectify the fault quickly. Sometimes, of course, the glaze is an absolute humdinger and in that case experimenting ceases and a full-scale batch to test its consistency is prepared for firing.

Assuming, then, that the basic glaze looks promising, it is usually necessary to make slight modifications to suit the ware. This may simply mean combining it with an already established glaze, as in double dipping, or it may require colour adjustments. Whatever form these modifications take, the potter is putting his energies into making something that is already promising into a success. He rejected very early on the outright failures in order to concentrate his efforts on probable successes. This is what professionalism is all about.

The beginner may find that all his first recipes are failures and it is not until the twentieth attempt that things begin to look up. In order not to waste time, it is important to record those recipes that do not work. More productive energy can then be spent on successful glazes by experimenting with colour or, less often, opacity and mattness. If two or more glazes work well, try putting

If the plastic clay can easily be converted to a casting slip then this is a convenient way of testing glazes on vertical surfaces. A cylindrical one, part mould is all that is necessary (height 3 inches).

11

one on another or mixing them in different proportions. It is reasonable to expect that two glazes which work in isolation will work in combination. And while it is not inevitably successful, it is well worth a try. This is building on 'strengths'. These sort of experiments can equally well be applied to glazes obtained from manufacturers. They are usually safe functional glazes and therefore have their place, but few potters would be happy to be totally dependent on them. Just because a glaze is labelled 'scintillating blue', it does not mean that, scintillating or not, it cannot be played around with. Whatever the starting point, by experiments of this kind a good basic glaze can be made to do as much work as possible. It is quite likely, in fact, that only one good glaze recipe will be needed. If you have your own studio, the fewer the glazes the better, usually.

It is quite likely that simply by adding one or two things to an original basic glaze the potter will find all the variety he needs.

I started this section by supposing that an established potter wanted to derive a new glaze. This is in practice quite rare, for if his established lines sell he has no need for shots in the dark. It is usually only in educational establishments that time and motivation exist for experiments. If the studio potter wants different visual effects, it is often more convenient to modify glazes that he knows already work.

First glaze experiments

Get hold of good glaze recipes from a practising potter or art school, having first studied the glazes, the clay they are on and the conditions in which they are used. If you have no such contacts you may have to search for book recipes. This is often a lengthy business, but eventually something should turn up.

Try to consider each glaze effect from two standpoints: first ask yourself 'is it a good glaze?', and then, 'will it stand modifications?' Some glazes seem to be so excellent in themselves that any deviation from the conditions that caused the excellence give awful results. This can be due to a difference of clay body, glaze thickness, firing temperature, the way the glaze flows on a particular pot, as well as changes in the recipe. Glazes often less immediately attractive are capable of considerable adaptation with the advantage of giving a variety of effects within one basic glaze batch.

Only experience will show which glazes might be usefully modified and the next two chapters explore these possibilities, using chemical additions. Before looking at these, however, let me introduce some simple experiments that the beginner could try, given one or two established glazes.

1 *Try the glazes on different clays.* The results may vary considerably, particularly in the stoneware range. This is not very surprising when you consider the chemical tie-up between clays and glazes and the variability of clay bodies. (See Chapters 2 and 3.)

2 *Vary the thickness of application.* At temperature the clay body and glaze layers react on each other at their boundary, but some things in the clay — notably iron — bleed into the glaze from the clay. Naturally enough if the glaze is on thickly the substance has further to bleed to make any effect on the outside surface. In this way some glazes on some clays show marked differences between thin and thick applications.

N.B. (a) This also means that they show up finger marks and dribbles so that glazing must be meticulously carried out.

N.B. (b) Variation of glaze thickness will also occur on textured surfaces as the glaze sinks into the 'valleys'. It is therefore logical to put glazes which vary with thickness on to textured pots, and

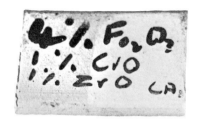

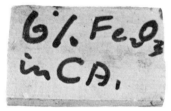

Reverse of test tiles showing sufficient data for reproducibility. CA is a reference number for a basic glaze. Information is burnt on in iron oxide.

Before and after firing glaze tests. Even in a black and white photograph you can see that the raw glaze bears no relationship to the fired glaze.

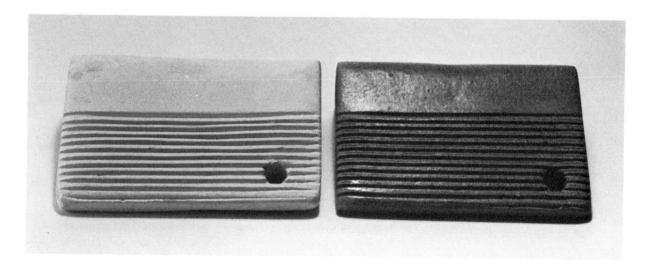

Celadon glazed stoneware of the Chieng-mai dynasty. Translucent celadon glazes unite perfectly with incised decoration. Surface modulations are translated into tonal variations through the varying depths of the glaze. *Victoria and Albert Museum*

in fact potters often approach the situation from the other end, that is, given a glaze which is known to show variations in its thickness, textures are put on pots to show this effect to its full advantage.

3 *Mixing glazes.* This, in ceramic terms, is quite a dramatic thing to do. It is not like mixing paints where, normally, oil would only be mixed with oil, and so on. It is more like mixing watercolours with oils because the basic glaze is different. Actually all glazes have so much in common chemically that this analogy is a bit extreme (though in the light of some results it may seem quite apt). Mixing glazes is instructive because it makes the potter aware of the basic glaze. He is forced to think less of colour, for instance, or of mattness. An experienced potter would not, for example, expect to mix a shiny blue glaze with a matt brown glaze in order to get a semi-matt muted blue result. The chemistry is just too complicated for such a simplistic approach and it is the chemistry of the basic glazes, just as much as of the colouring or matting agents, which causes the final results. Fortunately it is not necessary to understand why a certain result occurs from mixing glazes — you either use it or get rid of it. I have, for example, a glaze which was bought as 'blue'. When I tried it, it came out brown and under no circumstances would it produce blue. One day a student showed me a beautiful blue bowl which had just come out of a firing, she had achieved this by putting a transparent glaze under the blue. This makes nonsense if you think in terms of paints, so don't. Remember that glazes are three dimensional entities in their own right and that when they are producing the effects that you eventually see they are molten and running over clay surfaces and all the while each ingredient is having its own complex effect upon every other ingredient. By mixing two different glazes you considerably multiply these interactions.
N.B. Glazes do not have to be mixed in the ratio of 1 : 1. At least try 1 : 3, i.e. 25 per cent and 75 per cent.
The example I gave above leads on to the fourth experiment:

4 *Putting one glaze on top of another.* The results are usually less violent than those achieved from mixing the glazes. Two effects are possible depending on which glaze is put on first. The main drawbacks are (a) the results will vary as the precise thickness of each glaze is likely to be of crucial importance (b) two glaze layers usually mean a considerable increase in overall glaze thickness.

Victorian tile with relief clay moulding causing variation in glaze thickness. Most old earthenware will show crazing in the glaze, especially when thickly applied as here.

This in turn means that in firing the glazes tend to avalanche down vertical clay surfaces and ruin pots and kiln shelves. This danger is increased by the possible increase in overall fluxing potential (see Chapter 2).

Warning
Whenever experimenting with glazes — especially as in 3 and 4 above, take the following precautions:

1 Do plenty of glaze tests before committing the glaze to a serious piece of work. Do not rely on one test tile.

2 Test vertical as well as horizontal surfaces as most disasters in kilns are caused by glazes running off a vertical surface on to a kiln shelf.

3 Apply the test glaze to the top half of the vertical test surface to allow it plenty of scope for running down the rest of the clay.

Complex use of wax resist combined with white and dark brown stoneware glazes (*opposite*).

4 Place the test piece on an old broken piece of kiln shelf so that if the glaze does run it will not damage valuable kiln furniture.

5 Do not put a test piece on the edge of a kiln shelf — many pots are ruined by test glazes flooding off the kiln shelf above. Worse still, the glaze may drip on to electric elements which will then inevitably need replacing.

6 Do not combine earthenware and stoneware glazes.

2 Experimenting With Standard Glazes

Before looking at what a glaze is, we shall consider how we can change it. This may seem to be putting the cart before the horse, but it makes sense in that we usually start experimenting from a basic glaze mix. Like an oil painter we shall assume a medium and then float colours in it, and generally play around with it. It is fairly easy to modify glazes in this way and is excellent practise for the beginner as the results are clearly visible.

We are thinking of a substance like window glass — shiny and transparent; this can be perfectly acceptable both aesthetically and functionally. In other words it can look 'right' and do its job, for example, contain liquids. It is the sort of glaze used in nearly all earthenware industrial pottery but the studio potter usually wants more interesting effects. He wants the glaze itself to carry as much weight visually as the shape of the pot.

What sort of factors will a studio potter investigate? In this chapter we will consider the visual options open to a potter with the chemicals that produce these effects. There are four quite separate directions in which a glaze can be taken:

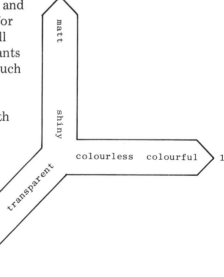

1 The glaze can be coloured. This produces effects like coloured glass bottles or stained glass.

2 The glaze can be made translucent by adding opacifiers, which cloud it until it finally becomes opaque. This could be thought of as adding the colour 'white', but I think it is easier to deal with colour and opacity separately.

3 The surface can be shiny or matt or anything in between. The first two directions deal with the substance of the glaze whereas the degree of mattness need be only a surface effect.

There are different chemicals that can be added to the basic glaze to take it in any of these three directions. They can, therefore, be considered quite independently.

4 The glaze can be 'flecked' or 'broken'. This fourth direction depends to some extent on the way the chemicals are added in 1, 2 and 3 as well as on the basic glaze and recipe. It can give a colour fleck or shiny/matt fleck or it may rely on the relative thickness of the glaze.

Scales which have built in small weight gradations as shown here are extremely useful. It is always the small independent weights that get lost!

Colouring agents

Colour is important, and should be considered carefully in relation to all other factors. An inappropriate or over-dominant colour will make a pot look 'plastic'. Generally, quieter colours are more successful because they do not claim one's whole attention and in consequence give importance to other glaze qualities.

Basically there are only four metals that are commonly used to give colour: cobalt, manganese, iron and copper. Exactly what sort of colour they give will depend on the amount of each oxide present, the kiln atmosphere and the type of glaze they are in. The most stable colour is cobalt. It will usually give blue in quantities up to about 2 per cent; after that the colour is black. Thus in oxidation or reduction, lead or sodium-based glaze, earthenware or stoneware, its colour is usually blue. Manganese is less exciting as a colour. At earthenware temperatures in lead glazes it is at its most beautiful and can be an iridescent brown-purple. At other tempera-

A test tile with a hole in it is useful for tying the bucket handle of the same glaze mix when an experimental glaze is adapted as a standard studio glaze. An immediate record is then always to hand.

Test tiles with a right angle bend in them can be fired vertically. Many ceramic objects (e.g. mugs, pots, lamp bases) require the glaze to be effective in the vertical plane. Horizontal glaze tests can be deceptive. Texturing on the tile increases the descriptiveness of a glaze's visual properties.

tures and in varying atmospheres the colour is brown or dirty brown. Iron we know already to some extent. In percentages of about 6 per cent it produces the typical rust red that we associate with terracotta flower pots and brown slip. In smaller quantities the rust becomes paler until it is a straw or honey colour. In greater quantities up to about 10 per cent, it produces brown black. Copper can give a considerable range of colours from blue-green to red. The colour is dependent upon not only the fluxes in the basic glaze, but also upon the kiln atmosphere.

Oxidation and reduction

The foregoing assumes one condition which would never occur to the layman and which is always difficult for the non-scientist to grasp. This condition is a plentiful supply of oxygen. This occurs naturally in the atmosphere so iron rusts to red, i.e. is oxidized and becomes red iron oxide in our common experience. There is normally a plentiful supply inside an electric kiln, and so glazes and clays bearing iron come out honey, red or brown, depending on the amount of iron present.

However, in non-electric kilns the heat is caused by something burning, usually gas, oil or wood. Burning means the reaction of the fuel with oxygen. Thus, gas burning means gas using up oxygen. If oxygen is plentiful then there is enough to combine with the gas to produce heat and enough left over to oxidize any iron around to rust colours. If, on the other hand, the supply of oxygen is reduced by effectively closing it out of the kiln it cannot fulfil all the demands normally made on it. It combines with the gas to produce heat but there is not enough to produce rust reds, in fact any red iron oxide in the glaze or clay has some of its oxygen sucked out so that it may react with the gas. The oxygen in the iron compound is thus reduced and the firing is called a reduction firing. Separated from a glaze, red iron oxide, Fe_2O_3, is reduced to black iron oxide, FeO. This process can be described thus: $Fe_2O_3 \rightarrow 2\ FeO + O_2$.

This reduction effectively doubles the colour range of the basic colouring agent, iron. It produces the beautiful greens and blue-greys which are typically associated with the celadon glazes. Even more versatile is copper which, in oxidizing conditions gives either green or turquoise, depending on the type of base glaze used. (See Chapter 4.)

When we come to explore copper in reduction firings, the colour change is even more dramatic for it is found to give blood reds, pinks or purple reds. Reduction firings have much slighter effects on cobalt and manganese. We can list the colours obtained from these four oxides as follows:

	Earthenware		Stoneware	
	Lead glaze	*Leadless glaze*	*Oxidation*	*Reduction*
Cobalt	blue	blue	blue	blue
Manganese	brown/purple	brown	brown	brown
Iron	honey, rust, red, brown	honey, rust, red, brown	rust, red, dark brown	grey-blue/ green, black
Copper	green	turquoise	green	red

Three points ought to be made about this table:

1 Lead is an excellent flux at earthenware, but boils at higher temperatures and so cannot be used as a flux for stoneware. This is why the lead/leadless grouping only applies at earthenware temperatures. (See Chapter 4.)

2 Reduction is normally only carried out at stoneware although it is possible at earthenware. Because of this, the colour change associated with a reduced atmosphere here assumes a stoneware firing.

3 It is interesting, considering the colour spectrum, that iron and copper swap places in oxidation. Iron, which normally gives reddish colours goes blue/green in reduction, while copper does the opposite. But the iron and copper reds are not similar, nor are their greens. It is evident from the table above that the kiln atmosphere is less important for the colours produced by manganese and cobalt.

Colour clock
It may be helpful to consider the following comparison between

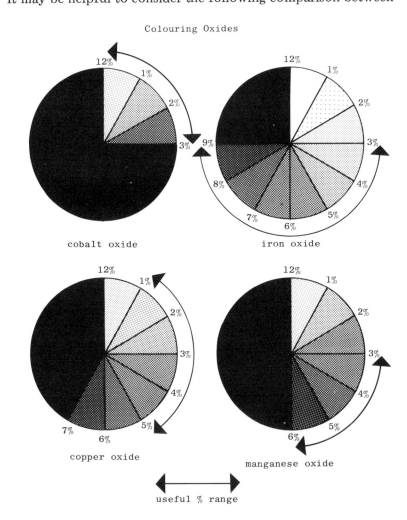

Colouring Oxides

cobalt oxide

iron oxide

copper oxide

manganese oxide

useful % range

the colouring metals and their relative concentrations in a glaze, using a clock face. If we think of the numbers on a clock registering the percentages of the metal oxides, so that the one o'clock segment shows the colouration due to 1 per cent of the metal in a glaze, the two o'clock segment shows the colouration due to 2 per cent, etc., up to 12 per cent, the colour wheels on page 24 result.

Twelve per cent is not a very large proportion and yet well before that level of concentration, the oxides are giving black, due to over-saturation. The actual quality of blackness will vary for the different oxides, with iron being the most likely to look reasonable. It may also be deduced from the colour wheels that iron has the most flexible range in concentration, while cobalt has the least.

It is not necessary to memorize these colour wheels since actual colouration results will vary in different glazes. It is important, however, to grasp how little should be used. More than about $2\frac{1}{2}$ per cent cobalt, for example, in a glaze is a waste of time, over 6 per cent copper, and so on. This point is particularly important when considering the actual use of colouring oxides; as mentioned earlier, it is often the case that those glazes which are subdued in colour are the most effective in hand and studio pottery. They allow qualities of mattness, translucency and surface 'breaking' to play their share in the overall effect. This is not the approach of the large tableware manufacturers where bright colours are common, but are localized. (See 'The use of colours in industrial ceramics', on page 307.

In this way the glaze presents a rich variety of qualities which set up their own relationships to each other and to the clay form beneath. Any single glaze quality which becomes pronounced (and colour is the most likely) necessarily diminishes the potential of the others, and the result is usually crude and sterile.

To avoid dominating colours, very small percentages, such as $\frac{1}{2}$ per cent of cobalt, 2—3 per cent copper, 2—4 per cent manganese, 4 per cent iron, are usual. Most of the colours achieved by using a single oxide in a glaze are rather shrill; more satisfactory results are achieved by mixing different oxides. The danger here is that because the overall colour density in the glaze is increased it is all too easy to end up with an uninteresting black or dark brown effect. For example, if a strong blue-green is wanted, the addition of a strong blue ($1\frac{1}{2}$ per cent cobalt) and a strong green (5 per cent copper) will give a black. It would be sensible, then, to at least

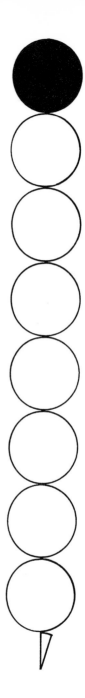

BASIC GLAZE
(100 %)

50gms
IRON OXIDE
(5 %)

20gms
COBALT CARBONATE
(2 %)

30gms
COPPER CARBONATE
(3 %)

40gms
MANGANESE DIOXIDE
(4 %)

A visual guide to relative pro-portions of colourants in the basic glaze. Each oxide is shown in a typical percentage *if the oxide were used on its own*. In mixtures of oxides the percentages of individual oxides would be substantially reduced. The mound of basic glaze weighs 1 kg.

halve these amounts to start with. It is rather like looking through colour filters. If you put a strong blue filter in front of a strong green one, you will see hardly anything through it, but if they are weak filters, they will tint the world a mid-blue-green. Mixing oxides is not like mixing poster colours!

One other point should also be mentioned here: variation in colour may be due not only to the opacity of the glaze, but also to the fluxes present in the basic glaze. As has already been mentioned, this is particularly noticeable with copper, but it is

A simple arrangement for sieving glazes. Always mix the glaze in water before sieving and always work on easily washable surfaces.

Earthenware and stoneware glazes may be readily distinguished by different coloured plastic buckets.

also true with other oxides. It should be possible, therefore, to alter the basic glaze recipe to adjust the colouring agent to an exact colour and if the potter comes to ceramics from painting, where colour is of paramount importance, this may seem a reasonable approach. However, the actual colour of the glaze is so secondary to other considerations, both practical and aesthetic, that a potter would rarely discard the basic glaze simply because the colour he has given it is unsatisfactory. In practice, the studio potter does not work to this end. Normally he has a basic glaze that looks interesting and then tries different oxides in it, choosing at last the combination which gives the colour most sympathetic to both glaze and shape.

Equal percentages of copper carbonate and copper oxide producing different colouring intensities.

There are many other metals which give colours of sorts, but most have drawbacks — for example arsenic and uranium — and in fact most studio potters get all they need in colour range from just these four metals already discussed. While it is possible to go into great detail about how the basic glaze modifies the colour oxide and articles are written on, for example, 'the effect of zinc on cobalt', most studio potters are not that colourist in approach.

The relative staining power of oxides and carbonates
So far we have dealt with metal oxides. If the metals are used in
the form of carbonates, it makes no difference to the type of
colour obtained, but does alter its strength. If, for example, we
take two batches of a glaze and to one we add 1 per cent of cobalt
oxide and to the other 1 per cent of cobalt carbonate, we might
expect the following result:

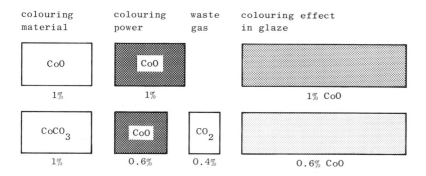

It will be seen that the colour is more diluted in the carbonate
form. This can be very useful. While oxides must be used in very
small percentages to give strong colours, carbonates can be used in
greater proportions to give a reasonable colour. Expressed in the
terms of our clock, the case of cobalt carbonate might read something like this:

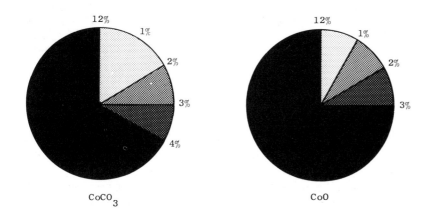

It is therefore easier to be more precise using a carbonate than an oxide or, to put it another way, it is not so important if you are less precise. So if in doubt, use the carbonate form rather than the oxide. Try them out for yourself to confirm this.

The use of colours in industrial ceramics
In a large section of the ceramics industry the all over use of a thin transparent glaze is common. This would seem to be very limiting, but the clinical white surface achieved is enlivened in different ways not usually tried by the studio potter. The point about a clear glaze on white clay is that if the glaze runs or varies in thickness in any way, it does not matter, it still gives a white surface. Any colour in that glaze would show up as thinner or thicker pools of colour as the glaze thickness varied. In mass production this random variation would be disastrous. Because the clay surface is so

Industrial onglaze transfer on transparent glaze ground. The white ground is the natural white machined clay body. The transfer provides a solid suspension for enamel colours.

conspicuous it is necessary for a pure white clay to be used and for an immaculate machined surface to be contrived. Thus the manufacturing techniques of slip-casting and jigger and jollying are preferred. The industrially-glazed pot, then, provides in the first instance a pure white field into which tightly-controlled, localized and often very bright colour motifs may be introduced, usually by the underglaze or by the onglaze processes.

In the underglaze process the same sort of colouring oxides used to stain glazes in studio pottery are used, but they stain what is in effect a high temperature glaze. This is fired on to the clay body. Because the underglaze itself melts at a high temperature, it is unaffected by the glaze melting over it, and the colour in the underglaze stays put. This sort of use of colour has a long history and includes our Willow Pattern.

The total coverage of an area with an underglaze colour is commonly applied by 'ground laying'. The general effect here is of a very evenly applied colour, but it inevitably lacks the depth of its comparable coloured glaze.

In the onglaze process, however, the colouring pigments are mixed in what amounts to a low temperature glaze. The clear glaze is first fired on to the body at about $1060°C$, then the onglaze or enamel colours are applied — frequently by transfer — and the pot is refired to about $820°C$. At this temperature the clear glaze is beginning to get tacky but is not molten enough to run, whereas the onglaze colours are molten and adhere to the glaze surface. Thus by careful arrangement of the glaze and onglaze fluxing temperatures, the transfer pattern will remain perfectly in place but, like a coloured glaze, will now be shiny and chemically fixed to its glaze background. The advantage of this technique is that as the colouring agents only ever get as high as $820°C$, less stable colours can be used. In this way very bright reds and oranges have been achieved which, if fired to earthenware glaze temperatures or higher, would burn out. It is worth noting, however, that as technology advances the temperature to which these colours can be fixed is increasing all the time.

Studio potters approximate sometimes to both the underglaze and onglaze ranges by using a crude colour agent — usually iron oxide. Under the glaze the iron bleeds through to modify the basic glaze in, usually, a very subdued effect, while iron oxide on top of the glaze can produce dramatic 'floating' rust effects. In each case the iron oxide produces its effect chemically at the temperature at which the glaze fluxes, and thus locally modifies the basic glaze itself.

The chemically complicated colours used by industry are available to the studio potter but are very expensive. However, the sharp divide between 'earthy' studio colours and sophisticated industrial colours and their corresponding methods of application has become less distinct in recent years.

Opacifiers

When considering the colouring power of certain metals, we did not relate it to how far into the glaze we could see. If the glaze had been transparent, then adding a colouring oxide would tint it rather like stained glass. We would look through the entire thickness of the glaze to the clay beneath. If the glaze had been opaque, then only the colouring oxide actually at the surface of the glaze would be visible and hence define the colour tone. So the effect of a colouring agent will depend to some degree upon the opacity of the glaze it is in.

Studio potters want glazes which are opaque or translucent so that in the finished work the observer is actually looking at the glaze itself, either at the surface of the glaze when opaque, or through a depth of glaze when translucent. The clay surface simply describes a form, while the glaze provides the visual impact. The scope for glaze experiment is increased by varying opacity and far more satisfying results can be obtained than with a transparent glaze. Random effects may be encouraged, giving rise to a spontaneity unacceptable in industrial ceramics. The opacity of a glaze is not quite as controllable as colouring, for many glazes, particularly at stoneware, will be translucent from the start. The celadons, for example, come into this category. And while it is always easy enough to increase opacity (or translucency) the reverse is rarely possible. Glaze recipes usually have a certain degree of opacity built into them and this is due to the basic ingredients of the glaze. If the opacifiers noted below occur in a glaze recipe they might be left out in an attempt to obtain a transparent glaze, but frequently the opacity is not that easily determined. As it happens, it is highly unlikely that a potter would want to make an opaque or translucent glaze transparent, so we can concentrate on increasing translucency.

Both tin oxide (SnO_2) and zirconium oxide (ZrO_2) are excellent opacifiers and are generally used for this purpose. Tin is the white associated with Delft ware and is a very pure white. Zirconium is more creamy and needs to be used in greater quantities; but it is cheaper. Small quantities of either oxide cloud the basic glaze to a translucent medium, and this gives depth when used in combination with colouring agents. For total opacity, 2 per cent tin oxide or 10 per cent zirconium oxide can be used. For translucency, $\frac{1}{2}$ to 1 per cent tin oxide or 4 to 7 per cent zirconium oxide. This is assuming that we start from a transparent glaze base. As with colouring agents, it is far better to test each glaze with different percentage additions of an opacifier before final commitment. Theory necessarily involves generalizations and each potter's situation is specific.

These two opacifiers are successful under all firing conditions, whether earthenware or stoneware, but other possibilities also exist. An opacifier is simply a material which will scatter light entering the glaze, often by maintaining its individual crystalline nature. At earthenware temperatures, if about 10 per cent china clay is added to a transparent glaze not only does it make the glaze slightly translucent, but it gives the surface a less watery appearance. Both these qualities are usually desirable in association with a coloured glaze and hand pottery manufacture.

One very beautiful stoneware variant in translucency (but not total opacity) is the Chün family of glazes. In these, translucency may be achieved by tiny bubbles appearing in the glaze. A gas is given off, but it is retained in the glaze due to its viscosity and a translucent honeycomb results. The bubbles inhibit the straight transition of light in a way unobtainable by other means, producing an opalescent quality. The effect cannot be achieved by the addition of materials to a basic transparent glaze. It is essential to have a Chün glaze recipe.

I have not attempted to cover all the possible variations of opacification here. These can easily be obtained from other books on glazes. However, if you only use tin and zirconium, you will never exhaust all the possibilities, nor will you be any less adventurous than many professional studio potters.

Shiny or matt surfaces

At the beginning of this section I mentioned four different directions in which a glaze can be taken, and theoretically it should be possible to start with a very shiny liquid glaze surface and gradually

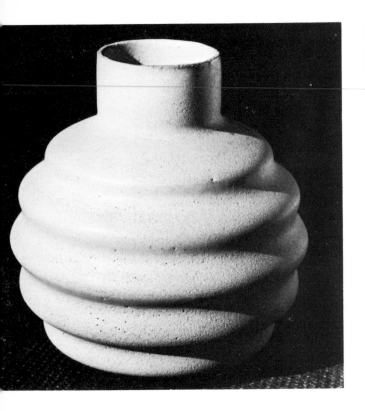

Two identical slip-cast pots (height 4 inches). One glaze is shiny and dark, which breaks from brown to black. The second glaze is matt, even and white. A useful exercise for examining the relationships between glaze and form.

take it through semi-matt to a fully matt surface. Commercial matting agents are produced for this purpose, but in my experience they are far from satisfactory. They often produce a scummy surface which unevenly covers the glaze and is most unattractive. It is always preferable to get hold of a glaze recipe for a matt or semi-matt glaze, for such glazes look right with matt surfaces, whereas derived matt effects usually appear unnatural. This could be because many matt glazes can be considered as underfired shiny glazes, that is, if taken 50°C higher, the surface of the glaze will flux out. In these glazes the dry surface is a function of the entire body and there is a completeness about the final result. If in this underfired state the glaze is beautiful, then it is immensely satisfying and colouring materials can be used to vary the basic effect. It is far better to collect glaze recipes of differing mattness and then vary the colour, than to have a nicely coloured shiny glaze and then try matting it.

If you must try matting a shiny glaze, try rutile first of all. Rutile is the geologically impure form of titania (TiO_2) and it is often stained brown with iron. In a glaze it forms crystals (titanates) with various fluxes and these effectively 'frost' the glaze surface. What happens chemically is less important here than what it looks like, and in the right base glaze the result is a slightly mottled, stonelike surface. This goes very well with hand-made work, especially if the surfaces and edges have a degree of 'bite'. Rutile can be effective in earthenware and stoneware glazes and perhaps its only real drawback is the fact that it has been 'plugged to

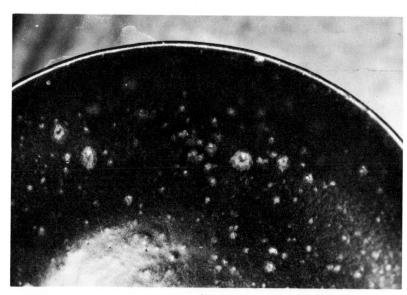

Identical glaze recipes and firings. One of the ingredients — silica — added as granular sand in the top photograph provides another dimension in glaze manipulation.

death' by recent studio potters. None the less, it is well worth looking out for a recipe with rutile (or titania) in it, if it works, it will be an excellent glaze.

I do not propose to consider here the chemical complexities of matt effects caused by crystals in glazes. Good matt and semi-matt glazes, no matter how they are produced, are well worth trying. First, because the definitive matt surface does not exist. It is quite amazing how large is the range of surface qualities covered by this one word. The second reason for trying several is that they seem very often to be sensitive to changing conditions. For example, iron not only colours but also melts a glaze and its addition — especially with semi-matt glazes — can cause the glaze to go completely shiny. Also, as mentioned above, many matt glazes are temperature sensitive, while some of the more exotic crystal forms require special cooling cycles.

Finally, I must mention one major drawback to matt glazes and that is hygiene. Because the mattness is caused by a (microscopically) rough surface, it is more difficult to clean than a shiny surface. If you intend making functional tableware, it is as well to use a smooth, shiny surfaced glaze — at least on the inside.

Broken or speckled effects

This is one of the most profitable areas to work in with glazes. Many of the best glaze effects are due to variations in the glaze. There is something entirely 'ceramic' in their quality. By this I mean that they are unobtainable through other materials, such as paints or plastic. These variations or 'surface breaking', as the effects are often called, can be due to a number of causes, some of which are discussed here.

Colouring agents

If the colouring agent is kept out of the basic glaze while it is being prepared and sieved, and added only at the end, then it may produce flecks of local colour due to the presence of large particles. If, for example, to a white glaze which has been fully sieved, we add 6 per cent iron oxide, then instead of obtaining a mid-brown all-over colouration, we should get light brown (due to fine iron oxide particles) with darker brown flecking (due to some larger particles). Whether these dark areas appear as spots or streaks will depend on the viscosity of the glaze, and whether it is on a

vertical or horizontal surface. It is also possible, of course, to sieve one colouring oxide and not another in the same glaze. Small variations like this can produce very different effects, yet if the basic glaze and colour are sound, these variations are invariably successful. The problem which often arises is that colouring oxides bought from pottery suppliers have usually already been finely sieved in preparation so that larger conglomerates of colour just do not occur.

A thick viscous glaze which bubbles. The thinness of the glaze beneath the bubbles allows the iron in the clay body to locally stain the glaze.

Small jug made from a clay body
with coloured speckles reacting with
a dark shiny glaze to produce flecks.

Crystal

Some matt effects can be produced by encouraging crystal growth in the glaze. When used in conjunction with a colouring oxide, colour variation results as the crystals themselves modify the colour. The most commonly used material for this is rutile. Particularly successful effects are obtained when titanate crystals are tinted yellow-orange by iron in a lead base glaze.

Other effects are possible depending on the type of firing, glaze and crystal growth, but these require specific glaze recipes. They cannot be controlled in the same way as colouring materials.

Glaze thickness

The colour and, very often, texture can vary with the thickness of the glaze. Some glazes are more susceptible than others, but the sort of factors affecting this variation are as follows.

(1) Iron in the clay body bleeds through into the glaze and modifies it where the glaze is on thinly (edges and rims) but has little effect where the glaze is thick.

(2) The thinner the glaze, the greater the effect of heat on it, so that thin areas may flux more. Such variations occur with most stoneware glazes. If a recipe for a glaze (often to be used in conjunction with a particular clay body) gives colour variations on crisp edges, it is worth trying it on heavily textured surfaces. There is something extremely satisfying in the way some glazes, by colour variations, echo the movements in the clay body and become visually integrated with it. The drawback for the beginner is that glazes with colour variation dependent upon thickness demand the highest standards of application. Otherwise the natural colour variations reflecting the clay surface are confused by irrelevant daubs (thumb marks, dribbles, etc.).

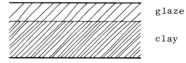

Iron bleeding through thin glaze layer to affect colouration.

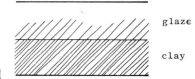

Surface glaze unaffected by iron in clay body.

Shiny/matt break-up

This, in my experience, is exceedingly beautiful and exceedingly difficult to reproduce in quantity. What is implied in this type of surface is a glaze which, if fired 20°C lower, would be all matt, and if fired 20°C higher, would be all shiny. Organizing this is very exacting and never entirely successful. For example, ware near to the source of heat may be shiny on one side and matt on the other; ware at the top of a kiln may be shiny, while that at the bottom is matt, with one or two successful pieces in between. Try the addition of about 5 per cent colemanite to matt glazes if you want to explore this quality. Again, following the earlier warning on matting agents, it is best to start with a matt glaze and add fluxes in different ways, rather than to add matting agents to a shiny basic glaze.

Practical tests

If you have not experimented with glazes before, the guidelines mentioned in the text may be usefully set out as a list of tests for you to try. I assume that you have access to standard glazes, either bought or already made up. You will need the glaze to be dry — or dried out if already mixed with water — so that you can measure percentages accurately.

Suggested procedure for mixing test glazes

1 Decide how many tests you want and make sure you have sufficient biscuited test tiles or bowls. (Let us assume two basic test glazes and six test permutations.)

2 Decide how much basic glaze to mix up for each test. One hundred gms is usually enough and it makes percentage additions of colours, etc., easy. Make sure the quantities in the recipe you are using have been converted to make up the total required amount.

3 Prepare two small mixing bowls with water (100 cc) in them.

4 Weigh out the first ingredient of the recipe twice — once for each bowl — and put each weighing into its bowl of water.

5 Replace any excess of the first ingredient in its container. It is surprising how easy it is to collect little piles of white powder, none of which can be identified.

6 Continue through the ingredients of the recipe to complete the two glazes.

7 If you do not know what the basic glaze looks like when fired, sieve one of the tests through a 200 mesh sieve. (A 100 mesh is usually satisfactory if all the ingredients have been commercially prepared.) Add more water whilst sieving if required, but be careful not to add too much. This is a question of experience and differs for different glazes especially between stoneware and earthenware.

8 Dip the test piece and ensure an even coating.

9 Use iron oxide to paint on the base of the test exactly what the test is. Failure to do this invariably means you are wasting your time, for after glaze firing anonymous test pieces are usually quite unfathomable.

10 Unless your test piece is very large you will normally have enough test glaze left for other additions, such as colour or rutile. Consider these as percentage additions, so that 4 gms of manganese dioxide can be regarded as 4 per cent if you mixed up 100 gms of the basic test glaze.

11 Re-sieve the test glaze — unless you are hoping for a speckled effect from colour additions (see page 36, Chapter 2).

12 Dip second test piece and label.

13 Make additions of colour, etc., to second test glaze, sieve and test as above at each step. If, for example, you are adding 6 per cent zirconium and 5 per cent iron oxide do tests (a) with the zirconium only (b) with the zirconium and iron.

14 The two remaining tests may be by further additions but try on occasions these two simple tests:
(a) put one test glaze on another (double dip the test piece).
(b) mix the test glazes together.

15 Enter the glaze and tests in another book and check labelling of test pieces. The six tests would look like the drawing overleaf.

The actual possibilities are endless. As a start consider the following:

1 To a transparent glaze add:
    (a) 2 per cent tin oxide, i.e. 2 gms tin oxide in 100 gms basic glaze
    (b) 10 per cent zirconium oxide, i.e. 10 gms zirconium oxide in 100 gms basic glaze
    (c) 3 per cent rutile i.e. 3 gms rutile in 100 gms basic glaze.

When you have mixed up each of these three batches and sieved them, glaze the test piece. With the remainder of each batch try adding some colouring oxides, for example:

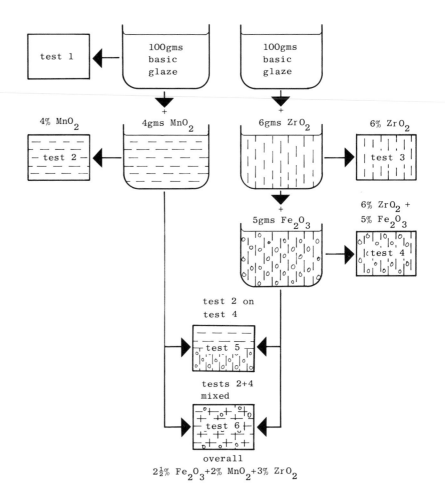

4 per cent red iron oxide *or* $\frac{1}{2}$ per cent cobalt oxide *or* 2 per cent copper oxide *or* 4 per cent manganese dioxide.

So the test (a) could have the copper, test (b) the iron, and test (c) the cobalt, for example. Thus the basic three test glazes have been doubled. As a final test try combining two of the glazes, especially the modified (b) and (c) tests.

2 To an opaque shiny glaze add:
  (a) 10 per cent industrial matting agent
  (b) 3 per cent rutile
  Then add colours as in the drawing above.

3 To a matt white glaze add:
  (a) 5 per cent colemanite
  (b) 25 per cent of a transparent glaze
  (c) any of the colouring percentages in drawing opposite either
       to the basic matt white or to 3(a) and 3(b).

4 To a coloured glaze try adding the colouring oxides in Test 1,
or remix a coloured glaze but leave out the colouring material,
then try adding different colours, opacifiers, rutile, etc., as in 1,
2 and 3 above.

5 Mix any of the test glazes with another test or overlay them
one on another making sure, of course, that the base glazes have
the same maturing temperatures (within 20°C).

3 A Look at Chemistry

Let us now get down to some scientific fundamentals. First, we are dealing with two different sciences, Geology and Chemistry. Once the different areas covered by each are understood, it should be easy to see which one is needed to solve a particular problem.

Geology investigates the rocks of the earth's crust. It is important to potters for a variety of reasons. First, clay is one of the important features of the earth's crust. Secondly, different types of clay have different uses in ceramics. Thirdly, like clay, glazes are dug out the ground. The difference is that glazes are mixtures of rocks. For a glaze, rocks are artificially blended so that the resultant mix melts at a pre-determined temperature and has a pleasant appearance when thinly stretched over clay.

Chemistry is devoted to the analysis and reactions of substances (for want of a better phrase). When analysing given substances, such as rocks, it spells out what they consist of, and in what proportions, and why they are there. Chemical symbols are simply shorthand ways of displaying the ingredients in a substance. If you happen to know what each of the ingredients can do, then you can make a guess at the overall effect.

As an example of the different uses of the sciences, let us take the fine yellow granules that we wiggle our toes in on the beach and that we call sand. Pretty obvious you might think, but we are in fact using a geological term for a specific type of rock. If you need to add sand to a clay or glaze, then you have an experience of what you are adding. Even if it has been ground down to a fine powder that no longer looks like sand, you do not feel as if you are dealing with science — but you are. In just the same way other sorts of rocks can be distinguished, but for various reasons they have been

Plate in tin-glazed earthenware (diameter $8\frac{3}{4}$ inches). Lambeth, early 18th century. Water based on-glaze colours must be painted on to unfired tin-glazed ground. Vigorous brush strokes are essential. *Victoria and Albert Museum*

Wax resist emphasis of applied decoration on white stoneware glaze.

Victorian tile. Coloured glazes puddling in relief decoration of the clay to accentuate design motif.

given stranger titles. Take the example 'Dolomite': this may sound unfamiliar, but it is simply a particular type of rock named after the French geologist, Dolomieu. The name has also been given to a range of mountains largely composed of this rock. So the cream-coloured powder bearing this label was once simply a lump of the Dolomite mountain range — or something very much like it.

In the same way, though for other reasons, a whole range of raw materials can be bought, many of which sound alien and most of which occur as a whitish powder. For most of the time all the potter has to do is to find a glaze recipe, buy the various raw materials listed, and add them in the right proportions. It is not necessary for him to know exactly what they are or what they do. However, if he is interested enough to go into what some of the raw materials are, this knowledge can be very useful in the studio.

Let us return to sand and look at it from the chemist's point of view. Given these yellow crystals, he would analyse them and come up with the formula SiO_2. This indicates that sand is a combination of silicon and oxygen. The relevance of this for the potter is that sand is not the only naturally occurring form of silicon dioxide or silica, as it is more commonly called. Quartz and flint are also SiO_2 to the chemist. In other words, the geologist looks around him and sees sand on the beach and gives it its name. He sees quartz crystals in granite, say, and flint nodules in chalk, and since they are formed differently, they get different names. To the chemist they all break down to silicon and oxygen, give or take a few tiny impurities. Consequently, if a glaze recipe requires the addition of quartz, but none is available, flint or sand would make perfectly acceptable substitutes. And the final glaze will not be very different.

The language of chemistry

There are certain key compounds which underlie the majority of a potter's raw materials. We have already met one of these, namely silica (SiO_2). Not only does it occur in flint, sand and quartz, but also in a wide variety of rocks from the common or garden, to the semi-precious, such as amethyst, opal, agate. The variations in colour from one substance to another are due to impurities in the same way that small additions of iron or cobalt to basic glazes give different colours. Since silica takes such a variety of forms it is not surprising that something like three quarters of the earth's crust is made up of this compound.

The next most important compound from the potter's point of view is aluminium oxide (Al_2O_3) or, as it is often called, alumina. Alumina links up with silica in the ratio of 1 : 2 thus:

This is the basis of clay. To be correct, it should also be mentioned that water (H_2O) is associated with this silica 'sandwich'.

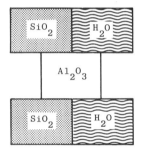

Under the right circumstances, two 'bricks' of silica naturally combine with one of alumina and two of water. If this seems improbable remember that rusting is not arbitrary. When iron corrodes, two 'bricks' of iron 'grab' three 'bricks' of oxygen from the atmosphere and in normal situations this is invariable. The arithmetic is very exact. Before going further, it seems sensible to explain here that in chemical formulae, the large numbers refer to the number of 'bricks' of the element immediately following the number. Thus:

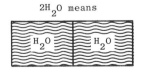

and clay itself is

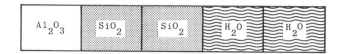

This is a long-winded way of writing it and the boxes are unnecessary, so we write $Al_2O_3.2SiO_2.2H_2O$.

The small numbers refer to the number of atoms present in each brick. Thus:

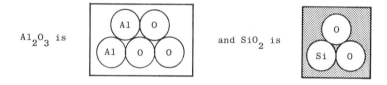

We could therefore write clay as follows:

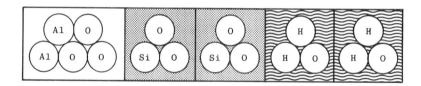

It is not necessary to know why two atoms of alumina should 'grab' three atoms of oxygen, while one of silica 'grabs' two of oxygen. Just as we accept *clay* as symbolizing the ceramic medium — we do not, after all, bother with who first called it clay or why — so try to accept that $Al_2O_3.2SiO_2.2H_2O$ represents the same thing in a different language. This is difficult, I realize, so let us look at it in a different way. Instead of building up from silica, alumina and water to clay, let us break down a piece of clay into its constituent parts.

Take a $1\frac{1}{4}$ kg piece of wet clay, enough, say , to make a good

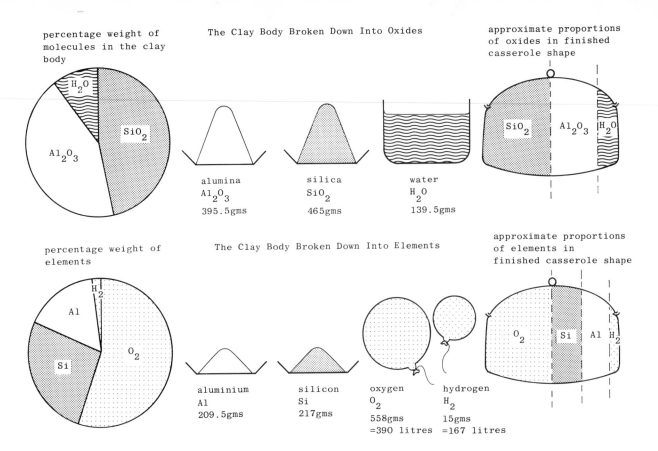

percentage weight of
molecules in the clay
body

The Clay Body Broken Down Into Oxides

approximate proportions
of oxides in finished
casserole shape

H_2O

SiO_2

Al_2O_3

alumina
Al_2O_3
395.5gms

silica
SiO_2
465gms

water
H_2O
139.5gms

SiO_2 Al_2O_3 H_2O

percentage weight of
elements

The Clay Body Broken Down Into Elements

approximate proportions
of elements in
finished casserole shape

H_2

Al

O_2

Si

aluminium
Al
209.5gms

silicon
Si
217gms

oxygen
O_2
558gms
=390 litres

hydrogen
H_2
15gms
=167 litres

O_2 Si Al H_2

size casserole dish. If we leave it to dry out as we would before firing, that lump of clay will then weight approximately 1 kg. Although we seem to have got rid of all the water, the formula for our 1 kg lump is still $Al_2O_3.2SiO_2.2H_2O$. This $2H_2O$ does not make the clay wet, it just makes the clay.

The basic chemical unity of ceramics

Alumina and silica are the basis of all our work, whether clay or glazes, and every other chemical that we introduce simply modifies these two oxides. For example, a small amount of iron oxide (rust) will dye the clay (which is naturally white) to the colour of rust and give the red clays that we all know and associate with flower pots.

Furthermore, many of the rocks that we use are basically not much more than alumina and silica and one metal oxide. For example, potassium feldspar is $K_2O.Al_2O_3.6SiO_2$. The only new part here is the K_2O. K is potassium (or potash). Otherwise feldspar contains the same basic building bricks but in different proportions. Those chemicals that do not include alumina and silica are mainly very simple like iron oxide, Fe_2O_3, or chalk, $CaCO_3$.

The reader who is with me so far is halfway home as far as the chemistry goes. It remains only to learn how these different materials affect the clay or glaze.

4 Creating New Glazes

We are now in a position to look more closely at glazes themselves. We have up until now mixed them, layered them and floated colours and opacifiers in them, but we have said little about the actual glazes themselves.

They are to begin with a mixture of powders in water which are deposited in thin films on the clay ware. After firing they are solid seas, like glass, which are tightly bonded to the clay body, and which have different colour and textural qualities. It is clear that the tiny powder particles have linked together and that this has been accompanied by a liquefaction of the entire mix. This is frequently shown by flow marks as the glazes have avalanched down vertical surfaces, puddled in hollows or produced 'icicles' on overhanging forms.

These are the observable effects but what causes them to happen? In this section we begin to establish certain principles involved in glazes which it is hoped will provide a basis for fuller investigation at a later date. Taking nothing for granted, let us first look at the process of glazing.

Water and glazes

Dark stoneware Kuan vase of the Sung dynasty with crackle grey glaze (height 4 inches). 12th—13th century A.D. The excessive shrinking of the glaze is used here as a decorative feature. The effect of this 'crackle glaze' would normally be considered a glaze fault as the glaze fits the pot poorly. *Victoria and Albert Museum*

There is nothing inevitable about the use of water for suspending glaze solids in — alcohol or turpentine would do equally well as far as the glazing process is concerned, but these would not seriously be considered for four main reasons:

1　Water is cheap
2　It evaporates relatively slowly

3　It is non-toxic
4　It is non-inflammable.

Measham pottery teapot, late 19th century. A combination of red clay with white applied decoration, plus colouring oxides produce a lively effect in spite of the basic simple transparent glaze. *Victoria and Albert Museum*

In other words, the obvious liquid to use — water — has a great many advantages going for it and no other medium has been seriously considered until quite recently and then only in very special circumstances — I am thinking here of enamel colours ground in oil for on-glazes. It should also be mentioned that water has not always been used in the glazing process. For many years glazes — usually the simple chemical galena, which is the naturally occurring mineral, lead sulphide PbS — were used in a dry powder form which was dusted on to the clay surface. Unfortunately galena itself is poisonous and the dusty atmosphere caused by glazing this way was extremely hazardous to health. It should also be obvious that no control was possible over the evenness of the glaze layer. This process did have one big advantage, however, and it was probably this single factor which held back more sophisticated developments in glaze technology: it could be applied to the raw, unfired ware. A pot was made, allowed to dry and then dusted with galena; only then was the work fired in a kiln. Any introduction of water into the process would simply revert the dry clay back into its plastic form and the pot would fall apart. Thus, work like the slipware dishes of the Tofts and Ralph Simpson (see page 81) were only once fired in accordance with this established tradition. It was not until the eighteenth century that biscuit firing was introduced and with it the general use of glazes suspended in water. Biscuit firing raises the clay to a high enough temperature for chemical changes to have taken place which prevent the reversion back to plastic clay if the ware comes into contact with water. Flower pots and bricks are examples of biscuit ware and their stability to water is clear.

It must be mentioned in passing that raw glazing — dipping dried clay into water plus glaze is possible in limited circumstances. The shape has to be 'safe', that is, simple, the clay body must be suitable, the glazing must be done quickly and the work usually has to be on the thick side. Clearly, if a studio potter can work within these constraints he will save a great deal in fuel bills, and a number of contemporary potters are succeeding in this.

Once biscuit firing had been introduced and the fired pot glazed by dipping into water and glaze, the advantages became obvious. First because the water is absorbed evenly into an evenly fired pot, the glaze is deposited evenly all over the surface during the dipping process.

Secondly, more than one material could be used in the glaze

itself. Although galena was dusted as evenly as possible in the old process, by placing it first in water it was possible to add other ingredients to vary the effects of galena in a very controlled way. The dry ingredient could be weighed, ground and thoroughly mixed in precise ratios which remained constant in water. In this way, the whole technology of varying glazes to get rid of faults or diversify glaze effects became possible. It is in this tradition that we find ourselves and it is up to us to make of it what we can.

Water is not an ideal medium, however, and its limitations should be recognized.

Disadvantages of water-based glazing techniques
The first disadvantage is that of evaporation. Although we have mentioned that evaporation is relatively slow, it is not negligible. If lids are not kept on buckets of glazes then the proportions of glaze to water are upset by evaporation. If glazes are used communally, the mixture should always be checked before glazing. There is nothing inevitable about the state of a glaze in a bucket. If it is too thick, add water — if it is too thin, let it stand for an hour then pour off the surplus water. In short, get it right for yourself.

The second disadvantage of water is that it does not successfully suspend the glaze ingredients. Sooner or later the glaze will settle out on to the bottom of the glaze bucket. What is less obvious is that different ingredients in the glaze settle out at different rates so that to glaze a pot in a bucket of glaze which looks well stirred, may be to dip a pot in a mixture in which half the ingredients are sitting on the bottom. Once again, play safe and always stir a glaze well before using it. If a glaze settles out very rapidly and into a solid mass which takes a long time to work into a usable consistency, try adding 10 per cent of powdered china clay or, if this alters the glaze, 1% bentonite. The fine particles of china clay stay suspended in the water, forming a sort of three-dimensional mesh which tends to hold up the heavier particles.

The third disadvantage is that many substances are soluble in water. These include certain materials which, from their chemical formulae, would seem to be ideal fluxing ingredients, such as borax, salt and soda. This makes their use in a glaze very unsatisfactory. Imagine a piece of work dipped in a glaze which has one ingredient dissolved in the water. As the water soaks into the biscuited clay, all the undissolved ingredients are deposited on the surface quite normally, but the dissolved ingredient is carried into the clay body. In fact, of course, it is carried into the clay as far as the water permeates, which may be the whole body. The chemicals which you may be tempted to use, and which dissolve in water, turn out to be predominantly fluxes. This is, in fact, the case. So, by dissolving a flux in a bucket of liquid glaze, we are effectively taking it out of the glaze layer at the surface of the ware and carrying it through to the body of the pot. Not only is the glaze unlikely to melt but, more potentially disastrous, the pot itself is susceptible to fluxing.

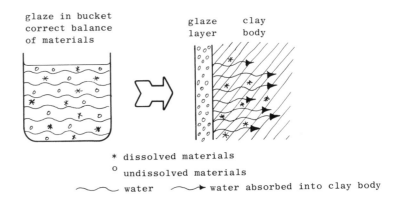

glaze in bucket
correct balance
of materials

glaze   clay
layer   body

* dissolved materials

º undissolved materials

～～ water   ～～➤ water absorbed into clay body

How a glaze works

A story told by the Elder Pliny describes how some Phoenicians stranded on a sand beach in Palestine constructed for themselves a fireplace made from blocks of their cargo, which happened to be natron. When they awoke in the morning the heat of the fire had caused the sodium in the natron to combine with the sand on the beach and — eureka — glass was discovered! This story is probably apocryphal, for glass dates back to at least 2400 B.C. but it illustrates a point. Glass is basically silica, and glazes are almost glass — glaziers put in windows after all. If you look at large sand crystals, or quartz or amethyst, you should be able to see that they are not too far removed from glazes. They are hard, shiny and translucent — all qualities typically associated with glazes.

A glaze, then, is largely a 'sea' of silica with a few other substances added, for aesthetic or functional reasons. Silica itself has a melting point of about 1400°C. But this temperature is too high for most clay bodies to withstand — they would blister and melt — it would also be expensive technology to arrange for kilns to operate at such a high temperature. It is far easier to add ingredients to the silica to bring down this melting point to a more convenient level. This is what the Phoenicians' natron did to sand. And today a great deal of the experimenting done on glazes concerns the achieving of the correct melting — or maturing — temperature.

A great many substances help to lower the melting point of silica and all of them have incidental side effects when considering its use as a glaze. Glaze experiments are concerned with juggling the various advantages and disadvantages of these melting agents so that the final glaze is effective and beautiful.

I have set out below a variety of possibilities to illustrate how silica is modified to make it work as a glaze. *These are not steps that you need to take practically yourself.* You normally start at the end of this chain of experiments, that is, with a glaze recipe.

Add pure silica only
We have already noted that silica stuck on a pot by itself will not melt. It is likely that if a pot with silica on it is taken out of the kiln, the silica will rub off as easily as it did before firing — the clay itself will, however, have matured.

Add a melting agent (flux)
The melting agent (or flux) will turn the silica into a molten sea at a certain temperature. Determining a suitable temperature which suits the clay and kiln can be simply controlled by adding varying amounts. Suppose 30 per cent is necessary to produce the desired melting point, then each time this ratio of silica and melting agent are mixed the desired maturing temperature will be achieved.

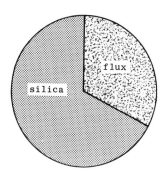

Add alumina
Clay itself is a combination of silica and alumina and in order to make the silica melting agent mixture compatible with the clay it has to be made more like the clay. Silica and natron may be suitable as a glass, as the Elder Pliny supposed, and it may melt at the right temperature but a glaze is not an independent glass sheet — one side has to stick to the clay. In practical terms this simply means that the silica/melting agent mixture is just too runny. At

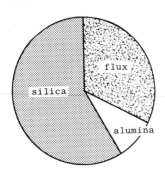

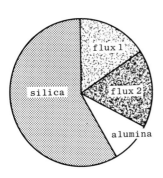

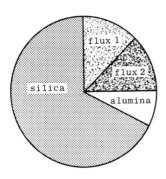

the correct temperature in the kiln the glaze runs like water and at the end of the firing the pot will be found to be standing stark naked with its glaze frozen solid round its ankles. Alumina, because its melting point is higher even than that of silica, helps to thicken up the glaze at its maturing temperature. Only a small amount of alumina is necessary in practice, but it is vital. It has a secondary role in stopping crystals (silicates) forming in the glaze. This is one reason, incidentally, why the actual achievement of crystallizing glazes is so difficult — too little alumina and the glaze runs, too much and no crystals.

Add more than one flux
The mixture of silica/melting agent/alumina may now successfully melt at the right temperature and stick to the clay surface but other problems are likely. Just as metal expands when heated and contracts when cooled, so clay varies in size with temperature (see Chapter 5). It would be an extraordinary coincidence if the simple glaze mixture we have now derived has exactly the same cooling-shrinkage characteristic as the clay it is sitting on. One of two possibilities is probable. First, and most likely, the glaze will shrink too much and as it stretches over the clay it will craze. This may not matter and, as it happens, a whole range of crackle or crazing glazes have been originated and used, especially in China. Usually, however, this crazing is unsatisfactory as the ware may not be waterproof and will also be less hygienic. The second possibility is that the glaze does not shrink enough and in this case each piece of glaze is nudging its neighbours for elbow room. The net result is that lumps of glaze flake off the surface.

In order to minimize these effects, two or more fluxes are usually added to make a usable glaze. Unfortunately one melting agent does not react like another; if 30 per cent of one melting agent melts silica at the right temperature this does not mean that two different fluxes divided into two 15 per cent quantities will have the same effect. These two may, for example, only need to total 25 per cent of the proportion of silica in order to reach the correct melting point. In exceptional circumstances, if too much fluxing agent is added it will start to raise the melting point. If this happens, try increasing the silica content.

Usually the more melting agents that are added, the more satisfactory is the glaze. It will be clear from what we have seen so far that any attempt to try to calculate a glaze by this sort of process is impossible — for most potters at any rate. Far better to use glaze recipes already in use and adjust them to suit individual needs.

I shall not pursue this series of hypothetical experiments any further but before leaving the subject I must mention other factors which should also be considered in choosing substances to be used as melting agents.

One of these is the solubility of fluxes in water. Suppose some of the melting agents were found to dissolve in water? It would be necessary to try to find ways of adding them so that they do not dissolve. This is possible usually and it is discussed earlier in this chapter (see page 55). If it is not possible then other fluxes — or combinations of fluxes — must be found.

A second factor to be considered is cost. If certain fluxes cannot be added cheaply then other fluxes might be necessary for a glaze to be economically viable. This usually means that the fluxes must occur in a convenient way in natural rock formations. Ground rock is the most common source of melting agents, which is the reason why geological names are used in glaze recipes. We talk of feldspar or dolomite glazes and this is really a description of the fluxes being used. (See page 69 and Chapter 3, page 50.)

A third factor influencing the type of melting agent used, and hence the glaze formula, is its toxicity. If a flux is poisonous it must be made safe somehow or abandoned c.f. the section on 'Frits' on page 71.

All these factors, then, play their part in determining a successful glaze formula. No glaze can be ideal, merely the best for a given purpose. Happily these balancing acts between different ingredients are not normally the concern of the potter. He is a practical man not a theoretician and he wants practical results, c.f. Chapter 1. On the other hand he should be aware that the jump from the simple silica 'sea' to a glaze recipe with ten different ingredients is one of hard necessity, both functional and financial. He can by all means deviate from such a recipe, both in ingredients and proportions, but should do so with care and understanding.

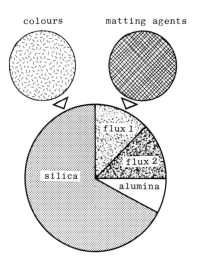

A final reminder here that all the considerations above have been directed towards producing the basic glaze, usually a transparent, shiny medium. It is to this basic glaze that all the visual modifications of colour, mattness, opacity, and so on, are added.

Some basic glaze recipes have, say, mattness built into them — so well and good. It probably means that the glaze is limited — it is not usual to build out the matt effect — but if it is pleasing, why worry? In general, though, a basic glaze recipe, unless otherwise stated, will provide only a modified silica sea no matter how many ingredients or how complicated the recipe appears to be.

Collect a number of different basic glaze recipes which you can modify. For example you may have:

1 Matt glaze — opaque
2 Semi-matt glaze — translucent
3 Shiny transparent — good craze resistance
4 Shiny transparent — gives good colours

These will all relate to one temperature. You will need a parallel list if you fire to both earthenware and stoneware temperatures.

Earthenware and stoneware firings

We have already discussed a number of different factors which go towards the evolution of a basic glaze. Since a glaze sits on a clay surface, the relationship between the two is also important in making a glaze. Temperature of firing, both biscuit and glaze, can be important here and this is what we shall now look at. The actual working temperatures are traditional, as are the titles 'earthenware' and 'stoneware'. There is nothing inevitable or necessary about them, but given that they are in current usage, let us see how they came into being.

We have already mentioned some reasons — glazing and handling — why biscuit firings are normal in the ceramics industry today. These reasons are sufficient for the studio potter. He wants a pot from a biscuit firing to be chemically changed enough to hold together when being moved around the studio during glazing and not to revert back to plastic clay when brought into contact with the water. It is found that the necessary chemical changes occur at about 800—900°C and so biscuit firing is usually established at about 960°C to make sure the entire ware is matured.

This is found to be a satisfactory temperature both for potters firing in glazing conditions to stoneware and also for unglazed ware such as flower pots and bricks (see Chapter 5, page 83). Next the biscuit ware is glazed and fired to a temperature in excess of 1200°C. Firing to this high temperature causes the clay body of the pot to begin to vitrify and it becomes impervious to water. More important for us here is that all the time the glaze is sitting on the surface of the pot it is being subjected to the same firing cycle. In other words the glaze recipe must take into account the fact that glaze and clay need to mature under the same conditions, in order to provide a dense watertight body. In this way a highly intimate fusion between the clay and glaze is produced and the exact boundary between the two is usually indistinct. There is also, of course, a chemical closeness between the glaze and the clay. If the clay body is vitrifying it cannot be far from its melting point so the extra melting agents required in the glaze recipe will be fairly small. Variations between the clay and the glaze will be more concerned with colour, translucency and surface quality.

Stoneware firing, as usually conceived by the present-day studio potter, is a fairly recent introduction in the West. Its chief application has been in the porcelain industry which in any case is not typical. A large section of the industry — especially tableware and sanitary ware — has concentrated instead on refining the appearance and durability of earthenware.

To this end a different firing procedure has been evolved together with a different role for the glaze itself. Most commonly a pure white clay is used. This is then fired to what is called a 'high biscuit' temperature around 1140°C. In this way a tough dense biscuited clay body is achieved which would not be possible at the low biscuit temperature of 960°C. The clay is fired then to a temperature which is in excess of that necessary simply to stop the pot from falling apart during the glazing process. Not only does this extra maturing of the clay take it nearer the density and toughness of stoneware bodies but it also shows up any faults. The chemical changes that take place between 960°C (the stoneware biscuit firing temperature) and 1280°C (the stoneware glaze firing temperature) are considerable and create severe strains in the clay itself. If the ware is poorly made, this may cause distortion and cracking. This is obviously extremely wasteful of kiln space. If, on the other hand, a pot is successfully *high* biscuited, any glaze firing below that temperature should be pretty safe. The clay has experienced it all before, so to speak. This is in fact what is done. The glaze firing takes place at a temperature of about 1060°C almost 100°C lower than the biscuit temperature.

A clay fired to 1140°C will be much less water absorbent than the same body fired to 960°C. In other words much less glaze is deposited 'pro rata' on a high biscuited pot than on a low biscuited one as the rate at which the water is sucked in determines the amount of glaze deposited. This situation suits the earthenware industry as it has generally evolved, for most companies use a pure white clay. All this body needs to make it visually attractive is a transparent shiny skin. Thus, the earthenware industry for the most part uses only transparent glazes and the thickness of a transparent glaze is less important than that of a coloured glaze. The glaze is enhanced by the immaculate machined surface. It sits on the clay body making it both shiny and waterproof and establishes an excellent ground on which to decorate such items as tableware with underglaze or onglaze colours. The close union between clay and glaze produced in stoneware firings is lost, so is the visual importance of the glaze, for usually in stoneware products what is actually seen is the glaze; whereas in earthenware the clay body is seen through the transparent glaze — the actual viewed surface is the clay. The glaze is functionally more important in earthenware products for not only does it fulfil the stoneware role of providing a smooth hygienic surface when required, but it also makes the clay impervious to water. Earthenware clay bodies fired to 1140°C are not entirely water-resistant — if they were, of course, they wouldn't accept a glaze, during dipping, for no water would soak into the clay and therefore no glaze would be deposited on the surface.

Whether the earthenware glazing is carried out in the formal way of industry as presented above, or whether it is more informal, as is possible in studios and colleges, it will be found that the glaze is less likely to craze on a high biscuited pot. This is partly due to the thinner layer of glaze on the high biscuit ware, but it is also due to the maturity of the clay body itself. By firing ware to 1140°C the increased hardness of the body forms a more satisfactory base for the glaze, given that both are subject to thermal and chemical changes of dimension during the firing cycle. As clay fired at 1140°C is not water-proof it is important that any glaze on the surface should be craze-resistant if functional wares, such as vases and mugs, are contemplated.

Summary

In an earthenware pot the glaze invariably sits on the clay, not unlike a varnish, whereas in stoneware (unless the body is very refractory) the fluxes melting the glaze are also attacking the surface of the clay. By maturing together in this way the stoneware clay and glaze are fused into a single entity and gain a visual strength.

Both forms of firing — and others including bone china and porcelain — have their technical advantages and corresponding visual and tactile aesthetics. For the studio potter interested in glaze effects and hand-production methods of manufacture, stoneware firings are usually preferred, but it would be wrong to consider stoneware as being in consequence more 'ceramic'. It is more obviously clay but that is a different matter.

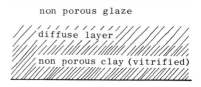

Fluxes — A colour mix analogy

To make the colour mix analogy easier to understand, all the black and white drawings on pages 63 to 66 are reproduced in colour on the inside back cover of this book. Please refer to them when studying this part of the text.

Imagine you are looking through the spy hole of three kilns (see Fig. 1 on the inside back cover):

dull red   yellow   white

Which of these three is the hottest? Which is the least hot? It is not difficult to tell. In all cases, as a kiln heats up, the colour sequence through the spy hole is:

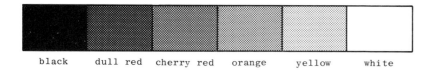

black   dull red   cherry red   orange   yellow   white

(See Fig. 2 on inside back cover)

Now let us change tack completely. Have you seen aluminium oxide? If you have seen aluminium then you have observed the oxide too, for it coats the surface of the shiny metal, causing it to turn a dull grey. If you collected the aluminium oxide you would find that it forms a white powder. This is commonly used in pottery as batwash. The symbol, you will remember, is Al_2O_3 and we will show it:

Silica, as we have already mentioned, commonly occurs as sand, which is usually yellow, so we will depict it as:

Rust is one form of iron oxide. It is reddish and we will show that as (see Fig. 3 on inside back cover):

Now, you are artists. What do you get if you mix white, yellow and red? I hope you answered that it depends on how much of each you add. Typically you would get an orange/red. Bringing these two ideas together we can produce an aid for remembering the melting effects of different chemicals in a ceramic mixture. Thus, while alumina and silica keep the melting point high (yellow/white), iron rapidly lowers it (orange/red). For example, if we start with clay (see Fig. 4 on inside back cover):

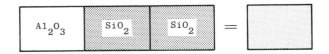

and imagine those colours mixed, then the sort of cool yellow we get implies that its melting point is high, for it is at the hot end of our temperature range.

Now suppose we add some iron oxide (see Fig. 5 on inside back cover):

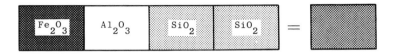

If we mixed these colours, we would get an orange/red which would imply a much lower melting point according to the temperature chart. Further, the more iron you add, the redder and redder the mix and, by implication, the lower the melting point of the mixture.

This is in fact the case. The red clays that are excavated are red because of their high iron oxide content and it is for this reason that they are used to make flower pots, bricks and roofing tiles, which require only a low biscuit firing to mature the clay. Fired up to stoneware they would blister, crack and finally melt.

Other mixes are, of course, possible. We could have, for example, one part iron, one part alumina and four parts silica, and so on. In this way we could obtain a whole range of yellow-orange-red colours corresponding to different melting temperatures. These mixtures are, then, glazes and can be put on the surface of a clay pot and fired to their calculated temperature. But the iron does not have to melt clay itself. It can melt any combination of alumina and silica and although most glaze recipes have clay in them, this is not inevitably so. Moreover, although iron is useful for our colour analogy, it is not the most powerful chemical for melting clay-related materials.

Colour analogy for fluxes other than iron
There are other substances which produce the same or greater melting effects on clay as iron, but they do not stain the clay. If we list them all in the red box, although they themselves are not red, we can extend the colour mixing analogy. For example, if we add table salt (sodium chloride) to clay, since sodium appears

iron	Fe
lead	Pb
sodium	Na
potassium	K
zinc	Zn
magnesium	Mg
barium	Ba
calcium	Ca

in our red box, we can assume that it will cause alumina and silica compounds to melt (see Fig. 6 on inside back cover).

Any of these chemicals lowers the melting point of a clay, and any substance with any of these fluxes in it will have the same effect. Look out for them in the commoner raw materials, such as feldspar, dolomite and whiting. They do it to different extents, however. For example, equal amounts of sodium and magnesium put into equal amounts of clay would not lower the melting temperature to the same extent. Their 'redness' in the colour mixing analogy varies (see Fig. 7 on inside back cover).

The relative melting power of the various chemicals can be shown in this way (see Fig. 8 on inside back cover):

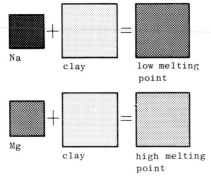

Na + clay = low melting point

Mg + clay = high melting point

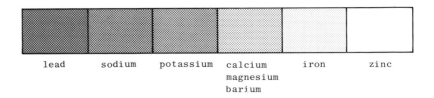

lead   sodium   potassium   calcium   iron   zinc
                              magnesium
                              barium

Broadly speaking, if you want to lower the melting point of a glaze dramatically, add lead. If you want to lower it less, add magnesium.

Fluxes and raw materials

Only in very particular circumstances would a fluxing agent be free from extra chemicals, as in the case of iron filings, for example. Most fluxes would be added at least as oxides and this is shown in the chemical formulae for glaze recipes or glaze materials, which express the fluxing metals in oxide form. Potters tend to use the term 'oxides' loosely to cover almost any simple compound which will flux or colour a glaze. In practice, however, it is not uncommon for colouring materials to be added in forms other than oxides, such as carbonates, while fluxes are very rarely added as *pure* oxides.

Metals are added to glazes to flux them, but they are not added as metals. And although metal oxides are the forms of the fluxes used in expressing the metals' presence in glaze recipes, they are not added in that form. How, then, are they added? They are added in the easiest and cheapest way available to the potter, in other words they are dug out of the ground; and however they are compounded in that state that is how they are used — this is implied by the use of the term 'raw materials'. (See page 59.)

Two examples can usefully be mentioned here. The flux calcium occurs naturally in chalk, as calcium carbonate and this has the formula $CaCO_3$. One rock in which magnesium occurs is steatite — also called 'talc', from which the famous powder comes. Steatite has the formula $3MgO.4SiO_2.H_2O$. Both rocks, chalk and steatite, are convenient ways of adding fluxes into a glaze recipe, but there is an important difference.

During the kiln firing of the glaze, calcium carbonate breaks up to give calcium oxide and the gas carbon dioxide: $CaCO_3 \rightarrow CaO + CO_2$. Think of chalk as a sort of ceramic honeycomb, that is, as a flux with a gas trapped in it. (Compare this with the section 'Relative staining power of oxides and carbonates' on page 29.) So that if we relate it to the colour analogy in the previous section we are effectively just adding red, that is, a fluxing agent.

If we consider steatite in the same way we can see that as well as adding the red of the flux magnesium oxide, we are also adding some yellow: SiO_2. These combine to give an orange fluxing effect.

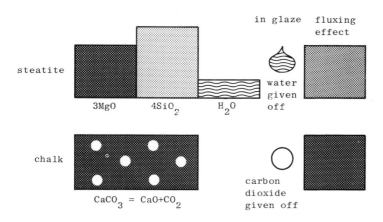

in glaze   fluxing effect

steatite

3MgO   4SiO$_2$ H$_2$O   water given off

$CaCO_3 = CaO + CO_2$

chalk

carbon dioxide given off

When we come to consider the fluxing property of a raw material we have two things to consider:

1 The strength of the metal oxide flux that we are adding. In the above example, is calcium stronger than magnesium?

2 Whether or not the flux is already diluted with silica or alumina. Chalk has no such dilution; magnesium has a considerable amount.

If a formula for a mineral has silica or alumina in it, it will not be lost in the firing but will go into the body of the glaze. Any other symbols — so long as they do not belong to fluxes or colouring oxides — can be ignored. Thus, you can forget sulphates, carbonates, sulphides, they will not materially affect the final glaze.

This may appear to be very complicated. But like much of the information I am trying to get across, it is hard to grasp, but easy to use. To put it in its true perspective let me remind you that you do not start from scratch when mixing a glaze, you start from a recipe. Whether or not a flux is linked to silica or alumina in any particular raw material only becomes important in glaze adjustment. Suppose, for example, that you have a glaze which has both chalk and steatite in the recipe and, further, that the glaze does not quite mature at the temperature you want — then you need to add only a small amount of flux to the original recipe in order to get the melting point down just that little bit. It would be safer in this case to add steatite rather than chalk. For in the steatite you are adding something which will bring the melting point down (magnesium), mixed with something which will modify its action (silica) and dilute the effect of the flux.

In terms of our colour analogy, if we add steatite we are adding magnesium (red) and silica (yellow). We are adding orange to the rest of the glaze which is basically silica and, thus, basically yellow. Orange added to yellow will make a yellow/orange, which can also be made by adding a tiny amount of red to yellow. This would be the situation if we added a flux on its own e.g. in this case chalk. You would end up with the same yellow/orange, but you would have to be careful not to add too much red.

The glaze would not be a total disaster if you bumped up the chalk instead of the steatite, but there is a greater likelihood of overdoing it. If, on the other hand, a glaze came nowhere near to melting at the temperature you wanted, then a hefty addition of chalk (5 to 10 per cent, for example) would make more sense. We are not dealing with absolutes here; nothing is totally right or wrong. Each potter must balance various alternatives in order to get successful results, and the more you know the shorter are the short cuts.

Adding fluxes in glazes — feldspar

We have already noted that in the chemical formulae for glazes fluxing metals are listed as their oxides. Suppose we came across the following glaze:

$$Na_2O.0.3Al_2O_3.3SiO_2$$

Now the apparently obvious step to take in order to make up this glaze would be to add:

1 lb (kg) of Na_2O to 0.3 lb (kg) of Al_2O_3 and 3 lbs (kgs) of SiO_2
    sodium oxide   alumina   silica

There are various chemical reasons, such as the solubility of Na_2O, why this approach would be unsatisfactory, but there is a more common-sense reason. Few potters are likely to have a jar of Na_2O sitting on their shelf. There are not convenient deposits of Na_2O, CaO, or ZnO, for example, lying around waiting to be dug up. They have to be refined and this process is expensive. It would be convenient if the chemical factory were extracting its Na_2O from a mineral whose impurities included Al_2O_3 and SiO_2, because potters could then short circuit the refining process. Although this isn't exactly what happens in practice many fluxes are found in combination with silica — e.g. steatite, just mentioned — and alumina. (See pages 59 and 89.)

Remember that one feldspar has the formula $Na_2O.Al_2O_3.$ $6SiO_2$ (c.f. page 51). Here the flux is naturally diluted in an alumina-silica compound in a very usable way. In fact it is so convenient that it is in itself, very close to what we want. It is not exactly the basic glaze recipe, but it is not far off. We would need a bit less silica and a bit less Al_2O_3 but this is easily achieved.

It is not surprising, then, that feldspar forms a major constituent of many glaze recipes. One well-known recipe, for example, uses 85 per cent feldspar — the remaining 15 per cent is chalk — and percentages of 50 or 60 of feldspar are not uncommon.

An important point arising from this is that you should expect high percentages of some raw materials. If a glaze does not quite work with the recipe you have, do not worry about adding a further 5 or 10 per cent of feldspar, for you are adding mainly silicates with just a dash of flux. This is in complete contrast to colouring oxides which occur in glazes in similar percentages to fluxing oxides (see page 71). The feldspar family of raw materials, all with slightly differing fluxing oxides and differing ratios, provide a simple solution to many glaze problems. Many of the fluxing oxides needed in glazes are conveniently packaged in alumino silicates, as Appendix 1 shows.

Non-feldspar fluxes

The potter is not limited to feldspars as a source of fluxing oxides. Fortunately other sources exist naturally and therefore cheaply.

The chief source of non-feldspar origin is chalk (or whiting or lime). This is actually calcium carbonate, which forms the basis of teeth, bones, finger nails and shells. Chalk, as you know, is formed from the shells of minute marine organisms. You may be concerned here that chalk is calcium carbonate and we want calcium oxide. Remember that when calcium carbonate ($CaCO_3$) is heated (even within a glass) it breaks up: $CaCO_3 \rightarrow CaO + CO_2$. The CaO (calcium oxide) is what we need, the CO_2 (carbon dioxide) is given off as a gas during the kiln firing.

Other naturally occurring deposits which include metal oxides of interest to us include:

Dolomite, a mixture of $CaCO_3$ and $MgCO_3$, often written $CaMg(CO_3)_2$. Like $CaCO_3$ it breaks up when heated to provide equal quantities in a glaze of MgO and CaO.
Barytes ($BaSO_4$), a ready source of barium oxide, as the sulphur and oxygen burn out, leaving this oxide, c.f. carbon and oxygen in chalk.
Steatite ($3MgO \cdot 4SiO_2 \cdot H_2O$), also known as talc (see page 67).
Ilmenite ($FeTiO_3$) can be considered a cruder form of rutile. The iron impurity is likely to give darker browns in a glaze than rutile.
Magnetite (Fe_3O_4) is a mineral form of iron oxide. This means that instead of it appearing as a flaky powder, like rust, it has the solidity of rock.

Frits

The convenience of being able to add fluxes in association with silica, as in feldspar, has lead to the manufacture of compounds which parallel the feldspars, but which use other fluxes and ratios. The most important are the silicates of lead. Lead is poisonous, so are all its oxides, but lead in association with silica is not readily absorbed into the blood stream. The main forms are lead bisilicate and lead sesquisilicate. These are known as frits and are chemically very close to lead glass.

Just as lead frits are similar to lead glass, so the sodium equivalent to soda glass exists. It may seem unnecessary to link sodium with silica artificially when feldspar does it naturally, but it is done to achieve a higher percentage of sodium in relation to silica.

By artificially forming compounds of fluxes in this way, large amounts of flux can be introduced in a form which does not dissolve in water. This is particularly useful for low temperature glazes — from earthenware to enamels and Raku. As I have tried to show, the more flux added to a glaze the lower will be its melting point. Since it can be difficult to introduce enough flux using natural materials, frits fulfil a highly useful function.

Figure of Shakespeare in earthenware, painted in colours and standing on black oblong plinth circa 1790 (height 18 inches). Oil based glazes (onglaze enamels) can be painted on to the fired glaze surface. Fine detailing is possible but the overall effect may be harsh. (See plate on page 45 for water based onglaze colours.) *Victoria and Albert Museum*

Adding fluxing oxides and colouring oxides in glazes — a comparison

Whereas the fluxing oxides are usually already diluted with silica and alumina in glaze-type proportions, colouring oxides, as we have seen, are usually isolated. So, if a brown glaze actually consisted of the following percentages:

6% sodium oxide, 1% alumina, 87% silica and 6% iron oxide

it is probable that the actual recipe of the glaze would be most conveniently arranged so that the sodium came packaged in an alumina and silica raw material. Thus, the composition might read:

	sodium oxide	*alumina*	*silica*	*iron oxide*
feldspar 47%	6%	1%	40%	
sand 47%			47%	
iron oxide 6%				6%

This should suffice to illustrate how small additions of fluxing oxides are disguised in a large percentage of raw materials, whereas the colouring oxides are actually added as small percentages. In short, when experimenting with glazes, raw materials which add fluxes can be varied by percentages of 5—10 per cent at a time, but the colouring oxides take much smaller jumps e.g. 1—2 per cent.

Just as fluxes are normally associated with silica and alumina, colouring oxides can be diluted in a similar way. These silica-colour combinations are called stains and just as the addition of 47 per cent feldspar added only 6 per cent of the melting agent sodium, so the addition of 12 per cent glaze stain may mean only 2 per cent of actual colouring oxide.

An extension of this is to combine all three — fluxes, alumina-silicates and colouring agents. By juggling with these mixtures not only can subtle colours be obtained but their melting points can also be precisely obtained. Thus, colour stains with a high melting point are used as underglaze colours and colours with a low melting point are used as onglaze colours.

Summary

Deciding which flux to use
We have seen how a variety of metals have been found to lower the melting point of alumina and silica, and how they do it to different extents. We have also seen that different minerals contain different proportions of fluxes. It might seem, then, that the choice of a flux or group of fluxes to suit your clay, your kiln and your preferred maturing temperature is impossibly difficult to work out. This would be the case if we were not starting with a basic recipe, for which someone, by theory or trial and error, has already evolved a balance of fluxes with silica and alumina to form a successful glaze. Working from such a recipe, the most the potter has to do is to add a few per cent more of one or other of the fluxing raw materials if the glaze does not melt properly or, alternatively, use less of the flux if the glaze is too liquid.

Assuming that you have a glaze and something is wrong with it, what can you do to put the fault right, given the wide range of fluxes to choose from? Here is a list of guidelines for dealing with glaze faults. It should be remembered that what may appear to be a fault in the glaze may have some other cause: it is always sensible, therefore, to remix the glaze and try it again in case the proportions were measured out incorrectly the first time.

1 Do not use lead in a stoneware firing, as lead boils at 1200°C and will evaporate out of the glaze. Remember, do not use lead at all if possible, because it is toxic.

2 If the glaze cracks, crazes or flakes off, cut down on the sodium and potassium ingredients (e.g. feldspar, cornish stone, borax) and increase the calcium, magnesium, barium ingredients (e.g. chalk, dolomite).

3 If the glaze runs off the pot in firing, increase the alumina (i.e. add clay or alumina).

4 If the glaze crawls, i.e. gathers into blobs leaving bare clay between them, decrease the alumina (i.e. reduce clay, alumina).

5 If the glaze does not melt fully, increase the fluxes (e.g. steatite, whiting).

6 If the glaze melts too much, reduce fluxes.

7 If the glaze forms crystals, reduce zinc and increase alumina (i.e. clay or alumina).

N.B. A further complication arises when considering the use of lead. With copper as the colourant, lead gives a strong and inimitable green. Substitute sodium or potassium for lead, and copper gives a turquoise. If a particular colour is required, then in certain circumstances both the colouring oxide and the main fluxing oxide must be specified. As it happens it is really only this one case of copper, and lead or sodium, in which the problem occurs significantly, although you might like to compare colour variations with different fluxes yourself.

Historical examples of these colour variations are:

Copper in lead glazes — mid-eighteenth-century ware, especially in the cauliflower and pineapple teapots associated with Whieldon and Wedgwood.

Copper in sodium-based glazes — the ancient Egyptian clay figures of pharaohs, scarab beetles, etc.

5 Geology and Clays

In this final chapter we shall look briefly at clays. The main emphasis so far has been on glazes, for it is in this area that the student potter can most profitably experiment.

You know from experience that when you dig up a lump of clay it is not a clean white powder. It might be red or yellow, it might have lumps, or stones or even worms in it. In other words, it is not just $Al_2O_3.2SiO_2.2H_2O$. The neatness of the chemical formula simply does not exist in nature. That is not to say that chemical formulae are invalid, but rather just simplified approximations. I mention this because one of the reasons we might have for adding a particular substance to a clay could be that we just do not have any choice. If you only have access to red clay, you cannot choose whether you want iron in it or not, but it is just as well to have some idea of what that iron might do to whatever you make or glaze.

The formation of clay

It may help to understand how different clays come to exist by looking at the fairly haphazard way in which they are formed. Underneath what we call terra firma, there is one thousand miles of liquid magma. Sometimes it comes to the surface by breaking through the earth's crust. It can be dramatic as in volcanic eruptions, or — and more commonly — a gradual uprising over millions of years. When the magma is red hot, and under extreme pressure, it is stable. By the time it has worked its way up to the surface, if it does so slowly, it is no longer red hot or liquid. In fact, it is the 'normal' sort of temperature and state we expect of rock, for that

19th century Swiss cup and saucer
(Thoune), with coloured slip under
transparent earthenware glaze.

is what it now is. One type of rock formed in this way is granite, as found in Cornwall or the Caledonian mountains. More important for potters is the fact that granite is not stable. Stable enough, of course, for people living in Cornwall not to worry, but in the long-term (millions of years) it breaks down, that is, it suffers erosion. As you know, sharp, spiky mountains get rounded and the bits that are swept away do not just vanish, they form among other things, clay.

Wind erosion is less significant than water erosion as water — especially if impure with naturally occurring acids — is more destructive. This occurs for example, when vegetation decays at the bottom of pools.

Let us now take a closer look at granite itself. The masses of liquid magma which move towards the surface of the earth and solidify are pretty variable in composition. It is unlikely, for example, that a granite rock in, say, the United States, which solidified one hundred million years ago, will have an identical mixture of chemicals to a granite mountain chain in Scotland formed two thousand million years ago. However, there are certain compounds which all granites have in common, and the important ones for the potter are: SiO_2, Al_2O_3, Na_2O, K_2O.

There tends to be far more silica than other compounds in the granite, and when it is hot and liquid, we can imagine it as a 'sea' of molten silica with the other chemicals swimming around in it. As the granite solidifies, it crystallizes in a variety of ways.

This is why when you look at a piece of granite you see a speckled, crystalline structure. The different combinations of the original chemicals forming different crystals can be clearly seen. Let us imagine these crystals as 'bricks' in the granite. Water falling on the rock affects different crystals in different ways, dissolving some, dissolving parts of others and leaving some. For example, some silica crystals dissolve, some do not. Mica does not dissolve, whereas the big feldspar crystal breaks up in rather a complicated way. The water washes away the Na_2O and some of the SiO_2 and some water actually joins the rest ($Al_2O_3.SiO_2$) to form a new crystal — $Al_2O_3.2SiO_2.2H_2O$. This, of course, is the clay crystal. It is not quite so simple as this may sound, since mica and some of the silica crystals and various other impurities remain, but as feldspar forms the largest proportion of the granite, it follows that when the granite has completely broken down, clay crystals form a high proportion of what remains.

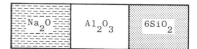
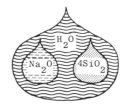

Primary and secondary clays

Let us assume here that our block of granite has been beneath a pool of static water which has gradually percolated down through the rock and caused the chemical changes. The decomposed granite, then, is largely clay but with certain impurities dependent upon its original composition, plus, inevitably, large quantities of silica. There are also likely to be quantities of the original crystals which have not decomposed — some feldspar crystals, for example.

The clay crystals themselves may be large or small, and in any

Pair of cats in agate-ware (heights 5 inches and $5\frac{1}{2}$ inches). Coloured clays roughly mixed provide decorative surface. Transparent saltglazed stoneware. *Victoria and Albert Museum*

Unglazed border tile, 19th century, coloured by slips. It has a tough decorative surface for flooring or outdoor use.

clay deposit a range of sizes will be found. If we were to go to a quarry face and chip away at the decomposed granite we would notice a number of things.

1 It will not chip but crumble — the action of water which dissolves some substances can be likened to sucking out the mortar from between the bricks in a wall.

2 It will probably be whitish in colour. There have been no colourful impurities in the decomposing granite and so it remains white. The best example of this in the British Isles is the St Austell region of Cornwall, where very white clay exists which is used extensively to form a fine white ware and high quality paper.

3 It will feel gritty due to the larger lumps of clay and the impurities of silica, mica, etc. It is for this reason that the clay is

of little use to the studio potter. The large grains provide a crumbly texture which cannot be shaped for it soon cracks and breaks away, in other words, it is non-plastic.

What the potter needs, however, is a uniformly fine-grained clay. While it would be possible to grind down or mill the large lumps of primary clay into small particles, or to sieve out the existing fine grains of clay, it would be very arduous and anyway a 'milled and sieved' clay is also formed naturally. This is known as 'secondary clay' and we shall now consider its formation.

Secondary clay
Vast quantities of rocks and soils get moved around within the continents just as the continents themselves move around, albeit almost imperceptibly as far as we are concerned. Indeed over the long term it is surprising to find places like St Austell — where the decomposed granite masses have moved relatively little. What generally happens is that water, instead of staying pretty well static and just percolating through the rock, sooner or later becomes a flowing stream.

This moving water does two things. First it separates the particle sizes. If you drop two stones, one large and one small, into a current of water at the same point, the larger stone will hit the bottom sooner and will be carried not very far downstream. The lighter stone will be carried downstream further and even when it hits the bottom may not settle, but be moved from time to time with the current. In exactly the same way, the primary clay when subjected to a current of water over a period of time is laid down into various grades of particle size. This gradation is very thorough as you may imagine in, say, a one hundred mile long river. Primary clay, at the source will have been broken down to very fine particles indeed by the time it reaches the mouth of the river.

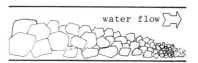

This same water course will rub the particles one against the other, breaking them down in the same way that a ball mill grinds its contents. So, over a period of time fine clay particles are washed far from the original granite site, larger ones are ground down and end up with the smaller ones, while particles incapable of such fine decomposition, like silica and mica, settle upstream. It would seem that Nature has provided the perfect solution, for clays separated and milled in this way are highly plastic. Up to a point this is true, of course, otherwise pottery would not exist, but there are reservations.

Suppose that the mud at a typical rivermouth was just such a quantity of fine pure clay, and suppose that we took a bucketful to make into pots. Although the clay may be ideal to work with, we may be able to throw it on a wheel for example, there are two things we have ignored. First, that there might be things living (or dying) in that mud. This might seem irrelevant if you think in terms of worms or bits of seaweed, which can easily be removed, but it is important to realize that organisms which have decomposed into a general sludge over millions of years and mixed with the clay cannot be so easily removed.

Impurities might also be added by direct contact with the rocks over which the clay travels, or indirectly through the water. The most important example here is iron. If, for example, the same river which was separating out the fine clay particles ran over rocks which contained deposits of iron ore, the clay would pick it up and become a red clay body. If it picked up large amounts, it would produce a clay which, when fired, produced the typical terracotta colour. This is fine if you want to make bricks, tiles or flower pots, but useless if you want to make bone china. It is also futile to try to wash out the iron — it is there for good.

Such organic material and subsequent geological additions — superimposed on to a clay which may be more or less perfectly refined — give us the whole range of clays which exist throughout the world. They determine whether the clay is plastic or non-plastic, red, yellow or white, high firing or low firing, and finally, whether it is valuable or useless to the potter.

In general, we can see that primary clays are non-plastic, white and relatively free from impurities, especially as extracted industrially; secondary clays are plastic, of variable colour and susceptible to impurities, notably fluxes.

Clays used both industrially, and by studio potters, are often blended by artificially modifying clays. By mixing them it is possible to:

1 minimize the disadvantages inherent in each and, thus

2 provide clays suitable for the variety of uses in modern ceramics.

3 maintain consistency of the mix even though the individual

clays vary within their deposits.

4 dilute good clays with poorer clays to obtain an acceptable and yet economic mix.

The effect of heat on clay

We need to look at the effect of heat on clay not just out of academic interest but because it gives us a basis for a firing cycle when managing kilns ourselves. It is unlikely, and highly inadvisable, that a complete beginner would be responsible for the firing of a kiln, but it is worth finding out about kiln firings through direct contact with those who know — for example, adult education

Slipware dish by Ralph Simpson, 17th century. Three-coloured slip decoration with galena glaze probably dusted on to the raw ware. Note the colours in the clays leaching through into the transparent glaze. *Victoria and Albert Museum*

or art school tutors. Students should always make time for involvement in kiln work. The brief outline which follows shows why certain procedures are necessary to ensure successful results. The actual chemistry and physics involved tends to be complicated, and for the most part can be simplified to one or two basic points for practical purposes.

It was mentioned earlier that water is associated with clay in two different ways. There is the water that makes the clay wet — and also plastic — and the water which actually exists in the clay crystals, i.e. that water which goes to make clay itself. The first behaves as we might, from everyday experience, expect it to behave: it turns to steam at 100°C. The kiln firing should, therefore, be taken slowly over the first 150°C in order to allow any such water remaining in the clay to escape. If this is not done, water may turn too rapidly to steam in the clay and cause cracks and explosions in the ware. As the temperature rises the heat attacks the now dry clay crystals themselves, and at approximately 350°C the water in the crystals begins to be given off. This process continues as the temperature rises to about 500°C. Once again, then, it is important to raise the temperature slowly to allow this water to escape. All this time, the steam must be allowed to escape and this is done by leaving the bung hole at the top of the kiln open.

At this point we must return to the discussion of the inevitable impurities present in clay. The most important of these impurities at around 500°C to 600°C is silica or quartz. What happens is that the heat causes the quartz crystals to change their alignments. Nothing is given off and nothing is added. It's a bit like Busby Berkley girls all suddenly doing a movement and there you are — with a different pattern. The importance of this is that the crystals get bigger — the Berkley girls spread out. When small particles of silica, sometimes in large proportions, throughout the clay all get bigger at around the same temperature, the stresses in the clay are bound to increase. Weak joins, variations in thickness, are likely to open into cracks. So again, keep the kiln temperature rising slowly through 600°C.

Other impurities in the clay will include organic matter which will burn up just as wood burns, giving off carbon dioxide. Depending on exactly what these impurities are, they will break down at any temperature up to about 800°C or 900°C. This is another reason for taking things steadily over this part of the firing cycle.

Ultimately, the clay crystals that have been dehydrated, begin to be affected by the temperature. They begin to melt into each other. Any fluxing impurities in the clay, such as sodium and potassium from organic matter, or iron from iron ore will cause the clay to melt at lower temperatures, just as with the glazes discussed in Chapter 4. Brick clays are of this type and sufficient melting of the clay crystals is effected by 960°C for the fired clay to be strong and durable. Stoneware clays on the other hand are made to fire to 1200°C or 1300°C, so that when they emerge from low biscuit firings, although they hang together sufficiently for glazing, they are soft and crumbly when compared with brick clays. In other words, few fluxes are present to melt these clay crystals and few crystals themselves have melted spontaneously so that the links between the crystals are few.

As the temperature of the kiln rises above 900°C more and more crystals melt, forming an increasingly glass-like body. This again closely parallels what happens in a glaze. At stoneware temperatures so many crystals have melted into each other that they form a body which is itself impervious to water, and in consequence a glaze is not necessary in order to seal the ware — unlike earthenware. The problem associated with this vitrification, as the process is called, is that, as the individual crystals are melting in large quantities, the entire pot is beginning to melt and this may manifest itself in distortions, cracks and even the collapse of the ware. It is because of this that the firing up to stoneware usually proceeds more rapidly once above 800°C or 900°C. There is also the energy cost to be considered for the quicker the ware reaches temperature the less the cost.

A further point should be mentioned in association with the melting of the crystals one into another. This is that the greater the extent of the melting, the greater the shrinkage of the ware. Up until now the only chemical change in dimensions has been caused by the quartz crystals which suddenly increased in size. All the spaces between the clay crystals which were once occupied by water or impurities, begin to 'cave in' as the crystals melt or vitrify. Once the vitrification of the clay has begun it may continue until the clay is entirely molten and shapeless. In itself, this contraction is not a problem but allowance must be made for it. Thus, teacups or casseroles, especially if intended for an exact capacity must be made that much larger if they are to be fired to stoneware rather than earthenware. Advice on this, as on the

recommended maturing temperature of your clay, can and should
be obtained from the manufacturer.

To sum this up diagrammatically:

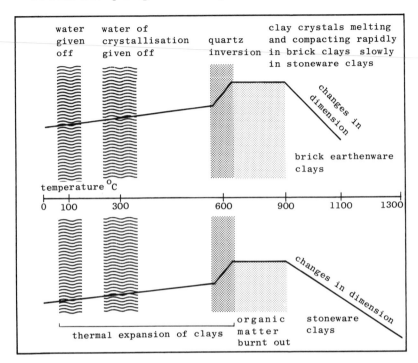

Experiments with clays

Compared with glaze modifications the experiments open to the
studio potter involving clays are very limited and unsubtle. This is
because slight modifications to texture plasticity, etc., are irrelevant in processing and indistinguishable in the finished work. Most
clays which can be bought are sufficiently versatile for general
manufacturing and firing requirements. In any case most clay
suppliers have a range of clays to suit different emphases in technique. For example, fine, highly plastic clays will be well suited
to throwing on a wheel, while more open clays, often coarser in
texture, are usually preferred for slab and coil work. The openness
and coarseness of a clay is frequently achieved by the addition of
grog to the base clay. Grog is clay which has been previously fired
and broken down to various coarsenesses. Its introduction into a

clay makes the clay shorter, that is, more susceptible to crumbling and thus less plastic. However, its introduction means that when the clay is fired a large portion of it has already suffered the various chemical and physical changes. It is in consequence useful for large, thick work where internal stresses are likely to build up, as it effectively reduces them.

There is also an attractive quality about the texture of coarse clay, both in working and in the finished result, but only experience will acquaint you with this. It is interesting to experiment with the addition of grog to a clay body or to its surface (more usual) either for functional or visual effects, and two or more particle size grogs are useful in the studio.

Just as iron oxide stains clay red, so all the other colouring materials will similarly dye a clay. Crude mixtures of two clays thus stained produce the marble effects usually described as agate wares. The major drawbacks to this are the uneconomic use of the colourant — you cannot see inside the clay after all — and its unpredictability. The colourant is very temperature dependent and what appears at biscuit to be pleasant, can be garish at glaze temperatures. The colourant may also be fluxing the clay body, in the same way that iron does.

More commonly, clay stained with colourants is mixed with water, finely sieved and applied to an unmodified clay body as a slip. The use of coloured slips minimizes the drawbacks inherent in staining clay bodies and the technique is used today both in studio potteries and industrially (e.g. Wedgwood's Jasper Dip) but not extensively.

The main problem of slip decoration is the necessity of putting the slip on the clay body when the clay itself is still unfired. In fact the wares should be no more than leather hard. The reason for this is that clay shrinks as it dries, and in order to ensure compatibility between the clay and the slip, the difference in their water content must be minimized. The danger of putting slip on to unfired clay is that the water in the slip will eat into the clay body and cause it to collapse. It is easiest to apply the slip to a piece of flat ware — a dish or plate — which is itself supported in a mould of plaster of Paris or biscuited clay, so that it cannot deform or collapse.

A further possible modification to clay bodies is the introduction of metal (usually iron) chips. These can range from iron filings to nails and will cause localized dark fluxed mottling. This is no more than an extreme addition of a colourant and is severely limited in potential, but it does produce an inimitable effect.

Finally, after all successful experiments on clay bodies, comes the question of how, if at all, to glaze the ware. Usually, as with the Tofts, the straightforward solution of a clear glaze application is used, although a thin opaque glaze can be effective if the stains burn through the opacity. The problem is one of balance; if the clay itself is unspectacular, then the potential for the glaze is limitless, but having arrived at an interesting clay surface nothing must be allowed to confuse or obscure it. The glaze then fulfils its most basic role of providing a clean watertight skin which simply enlivens the basic clay effects.

Appendix 1 Feldspar and its Related Minerals

The list below gives the names and formulae for some of the more commonly occurring raw materials. Although the names do not suggest a chemical inter-relationship, by looking at the chemical formulae you can see how close they are. You should consider the possibility of interchanging these raw materials in glaze recipes to see how much flexibility exists.

Albite
Sodium feldspar $\Big\}$ $Na_2O . Al_2O_3 . 6SiO_2$

Potassium feldspar
Orthoclase $\Big\}$ $K_2O . Al_2O_3 . 6SiO_2$

Calcium feldspar
Calcspar $\Big\}$ $CaO . Al_2O_3 . 2SiO_2$

Cornish stone
Cornwall stone $\Big\}$ $\left. \begin{array}{l} 0.30 \ CaO \\ 0.34 \ Na_2O \\ 0.36 \ K_2O \end{array} \right\}$ $Al_2O_3 . 8SiO_2$

Oxford spar
(potash feldspar) $\left. \begin{array}{l} 0.63 \ K_2O \\ 0.37 \ Na_2O \end{array} \right\}$ $Al_2O_3 . 6SiO_2$

Nepheline Syenite $\left. \begin{array}{l} 0.25 \ K_2O \\ 0.75 \ Na_2O \end{array} \right\}$ $Al_2O_3 . 5SiO_2$

Mica (Muscovite) $K_2O . 3Al_2O_3 . 6SiO_2 . 2H_2O$

Granite — very approximately 70% feldspar
(potassium and sodium)
20% quartz
10% micas, etc.

Basal biorite — very approximately 65% feldspar
(sodium and potassium)
10% quartz
25% micas, etc.

Note It is common practice for minerals with more than one fluxing oxide to have their formulae set out so that the total adds up to one, thus:

Potassium feldspar has only one fluxing oxide (K_2O) and is written $K_2O \cdot Al_2O_3 \cdot 6SiO_2$, which means:

$$1K_2O \quad 1Al_2O_3 \quad 6SiO_2$$

Nepheline syenite has two fluxing oxides (K_2O, Na_2O) and is written:

$$0 \cdot 25K_2O \quad 0 \cdot 75Na_2O \quad Al_2O_3 \quad 5SiO_2 \text{ since}$$
$$0 \cdot 25 + 0 \cdot 75 = 1.$$

The formula describes how much of each fluxing oxide is present for one fluxing unit. This is simply a convention and there is no advantage in trying to remember the figures or even that they add up to one. It is much more important for you to realize how few main actual ingredients there are. By juggling a few figures, Oxford Spar becomes nepheline syenite.

The actual ratios of materials present in each formula is subject to considerable variation and other ingredients are likely to be present as impurities: iron, titanium, magnesium, etc. So, once again, don't try to memorize them.

Compare this list with the following materials (naturally occurring or manufactured) in which fluxing oxides are linked to silica without introducing alumina:

Talc
Steatite $\Big\}$ $3\,Mg \cdot 0 \cdot 4SiO_2 \cdot 2H_2O$
Lead monosilicate $\quad PbO \cdot SiO_2$
Lead sesquisilicate $\quad PbO \cdot 1\frac{1}{2}\,SiO_2$
Lead bisilicate $\quad\quad PbO \cdot 2SiO_2$

Appendix 2 Molecular Formulae and Glazes

Glazes are sometimes set out in books in chemical terms rather than in lists of ingredients. The reason for this, presumably, is that by expressing exactly the proportions of oxides in the fired glaze, a greater degree of accuracy is introduced. I am not convinced by this, however, and in any case would not recommend beginners to involve themselves in it. Ultimately, of course, the more approaches open to you in your work on glazes, the greater your potential, but as so many books give glaze recipes in ingredient form it is simpler to stay with this form of describing a glaze.

Just as an example of the sort of difficulties introduced into the molecular formulae format, let us consider the following, admittedly specialized, example. Suppose a chemist analysed a given glaze powder and came up with this molecular formula:

$$PbO \cdot Al_2O_3 \cdot 2SiO_2$$

If you wanted to use this glaze you would have to convert it into actual ingredients; thus by a not very complicated process you might end up with the following ingredients:

Lead Silicate	$PbO.SiO_2$
China Clay	$Al_2O_3.2SiO_2.2H_2O$
Quartz	SiO_2

By adding them in the right quantities we would achieve the exact proportions of the molecular formula, and by firing them on to a pot we *should* get the glaze intended by the chemist.

The interesting point is that our original glaze powder analysed by the chemist may have been ground off a Ralph Simpson dish (see page 81). The original glaze recipe would then be nothing more than the lead sulphide dusted on by Simpson, the extra ingredients would be from the clay pot itself, and the sulphur would have escaped as sulphur dioxide. Our calculation of the glaze ingredients would therefore be in error. This discrepancy may or may not matter when reproducing Simpson's glazing effects, but you should always bear in mind that no glazes mature in isolation — there is always the clay body to allow for — and molecular formulae do not allow for it.

Glazes purchased from manufacturers are usually fritted, that is, the ingredients are melted together into a glaze and then ground down into a single powder. When the potter uses such a glaze he is re-firing it and would not expect gases, such as sulphur dioxide, to be given off since they would all have been extracted by the manufacturer. From the manufacturer's point of view a precise chemical breakdown of the glaze he is producing is essential in order to ensure consistency between batches. It is also likely that the glaze could be manufactured from a variety of different ingredients (c.f. our lead glaze above) and it is conceivable that different materials could be used depending on availability and cost, while preserving the same basic molecular formula. In my experience most glazes thus produced are unexciting and unsubtle. It could be that by removing them, as it were, one step away from the original raw materials, many interesting possibilities are lost.

For the studio potter such considerations are unimportant. If he mixes the glaze himself it is the raw materials that actually go on to the ware and they are once fired into a unique conformation. Molecular formulae are usually therefore only of passing interest to the studio potter.

Appendix 3 Bibliography

R. Charleston (Ed.): *World Ceramics: Illustrated History* (Hamlyn, London, 1968)

R. Fournier: *Illustrated Dictionary of Practical Pottery* (Van Nostrand Reinhold, 1973)

Gass (Ed.): *Understanding the Earth* (Artemis Press, 1972)

F. Hamer: *The Potter's Dictionary of Materials and Techniques* (Pitman, London, 1975: Watson-Guptill, New York, 1975)

D. Rhodes: *Clay and Glazes for the Potter* (Chilton, Philadelphia, 1959; Pitman, London, 1962)

E. Rosenthal: *Pottery and Ceramics* (Pelican/Penguin, London, 1949)

P. Shaffer & H. Zim: *Rocks and Minerals* (Hamlyn, London, 1971)

Starling & Woodall: *Physics* (Longman, Harlow, Essex, 1957)

Appendix 4 Suppliers' List

UK Suppliers

Clays
English China Clays Sales Col. Ltd., St Austell, Cornwall, do not supply customers directly with quantities of clay less than ten tonnes, but the following E.C.C. agents will deal in lesser amounts:

Anchor Chemical Co. Ltd., Clayton, Manchester, M11 4SR.
Fordamin (Sales) Co. Ltd., Free Wharf, Brighton Road, Shoreham-by-Sea, Sussex.
Somerville Agencies Ltd., Meadowside Street, Renfrew.
Whitfield and Sons Ltd., 23 Albert Street, Newcastle-under-Lyme, Staffs. ST5 1JP.

Watts, Blake, Bearne & Co. Ltd., is the other major ball clay and china clay mining company in the UK and they will supply quantities of clay above one tonne. Their address is:

Watts, Blake, Bearne & Co. Ltd., Park House, Courtenay Park, Newton Abbot, Devon TQ12 4PS.

Wengers, Etruria, Stoke-on-Trent, Staffordshire.
Ball clay BBV no. 1160W, earthenware clay 1401W, transparent glaze for earthenware 1491W.

Alec Tiranti, 21 Goodge Place, London W1, or 70 High Street, Theale, Berkshire. Grey modelling clay.

Podmore & Sons Ltd., Shelton, Stoke-on-Trent, Staffordshire.
David Leach porcelain clay, duo-clay, shiny transparent glaze for porcelain, P2108.

Deancraft Ceramic Supplies, Hanley, Stoke-on-Trent, Staffordshire.
(Craft Division of Blythe Colours Ltd.)
High-firing body stains, *inter alia.*

Potclays Ltd, Brickkiln Lane, Etruria, Stoke-on-Trent, Staffordshire. Red clay F1102 and black clay F1105.

Raw materials and pottery equipment
Podmore Ceramics Ltd., 105 Minet Road, London SW9 7UH.
Tel. 01—737—3636
The Fulham Pottery Ltd., 210 New King's Road, London SW6.
Tel. 01—736—1188
Ferro (GB) Ltd., Wombourne, Wolverhampton, Staffordshire.
Tel. 09077—4144
Harrison Mayer Ltd., Meir, Stoke, Staffordshire. Tel. 0782—31611
Degg Industrial Minerals Ltd., Phoenix Works, Webberley Lane,
Longton, Stoke-on-Trent, Staffordshire. Tel. 0782—316077
Wengers, Etruria, Stoke-on-Trent, Staffordshire
Snowhill Rural Industries, Great Easton, Great Dunmow, Essex.
Tel. 037—184—210

US Suppliers

American Art Clay Co. Inc., (AMACO) 4717 W. 16th St.,
Indianapolis, IN 46222
Arch T. Flower Co. Queen St. & Ivy Hill Rd., Philadelphia,
PA 19118
Bog Town Clay, 75—J Mendel Ave., S.W. Atlanta, GA 30336
Castle Clay Products, 1055 S. Fox St., Denver, CO 80223
Cedar Heights Clay Co., 50 Portsmouth Road, Oak Hill,
OH 45656
Ceramic Store, 706 Richmond, Houston, TX 77006
Clay Art Center, 40 Beech St., Port Chester, NY 10573
Cole Ceramics Labs, North Eastern Office, Box 248, Sharon,
CN 06069
Creek Turn Pottery Supply, Route 38, Hainesport, NJ 08036
Eagle Ceramics, 12266 Wilkins Ave., Rockville, MD 20852 and
1300 W. 9th St., Cleveland, OH 44113
Edgar Plastic Kaolin Co., Edgar, Putnam Co., FL 32049
George Fetzer Ceramic Supplies, 1205 17th Ave., Columbus,
OH 43211

Georgia Kaolin Co., 433 N. Broad St., Elizabeth, NJ 07207
Hammill & Gillespie, Box 104, Livingston, NJ 07039
Kick Wheel, 802 Miami Circle N.E., Atlanta, GA 30324
L & R Specialties, 202 E. Mt. Vernon, P.O. Box 309, Nixa, MT 65714
Leslie Ceramics Supply Co., 1212 San Pablo Ave., Berkeley, CA 94706
Metropolitan Refractories, Tidewater Terminal, So. Kearny, NJ 07032
Minnesota Clay Co., 8001 Grand Ave. S., Bloomington, MN 55420
Newton Potters Supply, Inc., 96 Rumford Ave., Newton, MA 02165
Paramount, P.O. Box 463, 220 N. State St., Fairmount, MN 56031
Rovin Ceramics, 6912 Schaefer Rd., Dearborn, MI 48216
The Salem Craftsmen's Guild, 3 Alvin Pl., Upper Montclair, NJ 07043 and 1042 Salem Rd., Union, NJ 07083
Sculpture House, 38 E. 30th St., New York, NY 10016
Standard Ceramic Supply Co., Box 4435, Pittsburgh, PA 15205
Trinity Ceramic Supply Co., 9016 Diplomacy Row, Dallas, TX 75235
Western Ceramic Supply, 1601 Howard St., San Francisco, CA 94103
Westwood Ceramic Supply Co., 14400 Lomitas Ave., City of Industry, CA 91744
Jack D. Wolfe Co., 724 Meeker Ave., Brooklyn, NY 11222

Index

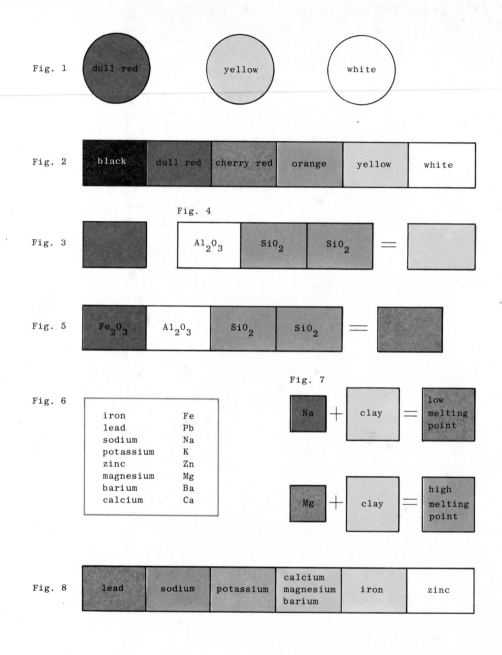

Fig. 1

dull red   yellow   white

Fig. 2

black | dull red | cherry red | orange | yellow | white

Fig. 3

Fig. 4

Al_2O_3 SiO_2 SiO_2 =

Fig. 5

Fe_2O_3 Al_2O_3 SiO_2 SiO_2 =

Fig. 6

iron	Fe
lead	Pb
sodium	Na
potassium	K
zinc	Zn
magnesium	Mg
barium	Ba
calcium	Ca

Fig. 7

Na + clay = low melting point

Mg + clay = high melting point

Fig. 8

| lead | sodium | potassium | calcium magnesium barium | iron | zinc |